MW00648913

THINK AHEAD
OF
DISASTER!

A Guide for Assisting Aging Parents

By: Eric R. Naegler
with Ann Naegler, MA, LCSW

THINK AHEAD OF DISASTER!
A guide for Assisting Aging Parents

Copyright © 2007 by Eric Naegler
Naegler Ranch Publishing

ISBN 978-1-60461-433-6

All rights reserved.

*Special thanks goes to
the people at Litho Printers,
Marty Jenkins, Chris Barnes
and Tonya Wogoman,
for all their wonderful help
in the publishing of this book.*

Printed in the United States of America
by Litho Printers & Bindery
Cassville, Missouri 65625

Contents

Forward

Life is an incredibly interesting journey! It is not all good or bad. It is a journey, continually moving from beginning to end. In some respects, it is circular. However, it does have a definite beginning and end. When we begin, we cry and poop our pants. We have very little understanding or control over our existence. If we live long enough, we cry and poop our pants and have little control over our existence. As we move along our aging path, we encounter events or issues for which we are not prepared. One of the biggest events for which I wasn't prepared was the aging and subsequent deterioration of my parents.

As an adult child with aging parents, I found little help available when I needed it. Society puts great emphasis on the "downtrodden." However, issues on aging know no economic bounds. There are all sorts of help available for low income seniors through local, state, and federal governmental agencies. There are multiple not-for-profit organizations involved in delivering care and comfort for low income seniors. All of these resources are needed and valuable, but who is looking out for the seniors who don't qualify for any of these services? Just having financial resources doesn't automatically mean you have the ability to care for yourself. We must make aging the issue regardless of our resources.

Many baby boomers will have adequate financial resources available as they age. Today, the boomers are faced with the aging and care of their parents. Tomorrow, boomers will face their own issues of aging. What goods and services will be available for the boomers as they age? How will health care be delivered in the next twenty years? How will home care be delivered in the next twenty years? Currently most people desire aging in place, remaining in their own homes or retirement living arrangements. As the boomers reach these needs, what will be available?

The vast majority of seniors today do not want to end their lives in a nursing home and the boomers will follow this pattern.

The most important health care person to enable seniors to remain in their homes is a physician. No in-home medical services are performed without a physician's orders. This should be the beginning of the cycle. Proactive, preventive health care for seniors would be far less expensive than waiting for a crisis to occur.

We need to develop a group of physicians who are "stay at home" advocates for our seniors.

In the stay-at-home model, simple mobility can be a problem coupled with transportation. Our stay at home physician groups should develop nurse practitioners or physician assistants that can "make house calls." If seniors have trouble accessing health care, take health care to them.

Helping seniors make their homes safer would help ease the booming health care burden. Preventing falls and accidents is easier than treating the injuries created by falls and accidents.

Transportation of seniors to office visits and required laboratory work becomes an ever increasing problem. We already have the ability to perform many testing procedures in the home.

Health Care campuses need to be more senior friendly. We need to develop centralized, easy to access, safe parking for seniors throughout our community with regularly scheduled shuttles to the front door of the appropriate care center.

We should ensure proper and appropriate reimbursement rates through Medicare, Medicaid or private insurance to cover physician related house calls. By streamlining and delivering proactive, preventive health care, both the physical and financial burden would be improved.

Physicians or those prescribing in-home services should not have financial ties to in-home service providers. We need to develop competitively priced goods and services to help our seniors stay home. The vast majority of services required to help seniors remain in their homes is assistance with daily living activities. The amount of time required for in-home medically necessary services is minimal. Even in today's rest home model, the vast majority of services are non-medical assistance with daily living activities.

We need to separate in-home medical services from in-home non-medical services. The medical model does not have the ability to deliver personal care goods and services on a competitive basis. The medical model is highly bureaucratic, over regulated, and its hierarchy is difficult to change. The ability and skill to understand and manage the delivery of non medical goods and services is different than those for the delivery of health care. You wouldn't ask your doctor to tune up your car nor would you ask a registered nurse to wash your clothes.

Locally our largest providers of in-home services are nurse owned or hospital owned home health agencies. Medical institutions have figured out how to justify charging over $5.00 for an aspirin. We can buy a bottle containing well over 100 aspirin at Wal-Mart for less than $5.00. Why do we think medical institutions are going to provide personal care economically?

In the future, Home Care needs to be delivered by separate providers from Health Care. Today, Health Care is trying to be all things to all people. Health Care should concentrate on the delivery of health care.

My mother died at home in her own bed at age 90. My father died at home in his own bed at age 92. I've completed this part of my life. I've taken the journey of which I now write. I know it is possible for others to end their lives as they wish as well. The purpose of this book is to share what I can with those still facing this journey. I have become so passionate about this issue that I've started a business to address this need in my area.

As I write this book, I'll turn 62 years of age. I'm not sure why I've decided at 62 to retool my life. The only thing I can think of is, for some reason, this is what I'm supposed to do. Although I attend church and am a spiritual person, I wouldn't call myself a "religious" person. I believe that many religions exist for some sort of control over our thoughts or actions. I believe we ultimately are in control of our thoughts and our actions. I deeply believe in God. I'm not hung up on what you call your God, how you address your God, or how you pray to your God. I just believe there is a God and It's for sure not you or me. I believe in the teachings of Jesus. However, I also believe in the teachings of others that teach love and forgiveness as well.

For me to complete my journey with my aging parents took a tremendous amount of faith. Continually, each day I ask God to be with me, to fill me with his Spirit, to comfort me, to do as little harm as possible and to direct my actions. I'm amused by the slogan, "What would Jesus do?" The more important question is, "What will you do?" You are still here, you still can make a difference, and you still can demonstrate peace and love toward others. If each of us does only those simple things, the world will be a better place.

The Bible offers very little about how to handle or care for the aging of our parents. Jesus died at a young age so his teachings do not address aging issues. Obviously, the Bible deals with how we are to treat one another and other moral standards. However, beyond "honor thy mother and father" there just isn't much to guide us regarding our parents. I believe that the 23rd Psalm is an appropriate scriptural reference for the journey:

"The Lord is My Shepherd; I shall not want.
He maketh me to lie down in green pastures:
he leadeth me beside the still waters.
He restoreth my soul:
he leadeth me in the paths of righteousness
for his name's sake.

Yea, though I walk through
the valley of the shadow of death,
I will fear no evil:
for thou art with me;
thy rod and thy staff they comfort me.
Thou preparest a table before me
in the presence of mine enemies:
thou anointest my head with oil;
my cup runneth over.

Surely goodness and mercy
shall follow me all the days of my life:
and I will dwell in the house of the Lord forever."

The Golden rule always applies and should serve as inspiration for all of us: Matthew 7, 12:

"Therefore all things whatsoever
ye would that men should do to you,
do ye even so to them:
for this is the law of the prophets."

My lovely wife, Ann Naegler, LCSW, MA, has edited and added notes and her comments to this book. I am grateful to have found such a lovely person after losing a wife after 34 years of marriage. She is living proof that there is "life after death."

I am fortunate to have a very loving family and adult children and grandchildren whom I love dearly. They serve as inspiration for me to make friends with my own journey through the rest of my life.

I am fortunate that God has granted me diverse life experiences that I may share with others. I sincerely hope that you are able to take something from this book to help you along this journey. I dedicate this book to my siblings who made the journey successful as well as my parents who lived and died "their way." One of my father's favorite expressions for planning for life was "Think Ahead of Disaster." I hope you take his advice!

Note to the readers: While I have used examples from real situations I have changed the names and made every effort to disguise the actual people referenced. I sincerely believe in respect and dignity for our elders and in no way intend to invade their privacy.

Dancing To Heaven

How do we want to live out our final days and years? This is important for each of us to consider.

We may be helping our elderly parents through their final years and be part of the sandwich generation with demanding careers, children at home, and parents who are in decline. If we want our ending time on earth to be a certain way, our parents probably have similar desires as well. Many do not want to end their days in an institutional nursing home at great expense. We need to consider our parents' wishes in their final years. How can we know if we don't discuss this topic with them? I had these discussions with my parents, so I knew they wanted to remain at home together until the end.

I ended up being their caregiver, a responsibility shared by my siblings. Did we always agree on their care? No. We all wanted what was best for our parents but didn't always agree on the specifics. Was it always easy to provide this care. No. Am I ultimately glad I did it? Yes. Mom was able to die in her own home with her husband of sixty-eight years at her side. It was as she wished. Dad also died at home.

Mom was a sweet, petite woman who loved music and dance. There were three sons in the family and one daughter. Dad took his boys to work and taught them to be men. Jane was Mom's little girl and Mother adored her. Mom took Jane to ballet lessons at Miss Lillian Zoll's Ballet School and watched her grow and flourish as a dancer. Jane was often the Prima Ballerina, and Mom was incredibly proud of her. Classical music and the ballet were a passion they shared.

Jane sat by my mother's bed as she made her transition to the other side. Several days later, as Jane drove to the funeral home, she looked into the sky and felt Mom's spirit dancing across the heavens, free from age, infirmity, and earthly bonds. Jane knew our mother was okay and happy now. In difficult times, we still feel her presence with us.

Is this an easy endeavor—living and dying the way we wish or helping our parents to do so? Of course it isn't. But it can be done in many cases. This is a guidebook for both seniors and those assisting them, who wish to see their loved ones dancing to heaven as well.

1.
The Issue Of Independence

I was visiting with my daughter-in-law's grandmother at a family gathering not long ago and the discussion turned to independence. Grandma made the statement, "I'd rather be dead than in the rest home." She's a petite seventy-nine year old woman who lost her husband about a year ago. She lives by herself in a 3,000 square foot home and keeps up a beautiful yard with multiple flower gardens. She does have mowing and landscaping help, but she does a lot of work on her own. She still drives and babysits her great grandson and cooks Wednesday night meals at her church for fifty to one-hundred people. Grandma is a very independent person! As we talked, she mentioned that one of her safety measures is the "I've fallen and can't get up" device. I joked that it wouldn't do her any good sitting on the vanity while she took her shower. She looked at me indignantly and said, "I don't take a shower, I take a bath." Her home is over thirty years old and I'm pretty sure it had not been fitted with any bathing safeguards. I read somewhere that the number one reason elderly people enter skilled nursing facilities is due to slips and falls. I believe the number one place in our home for a slip and fall is our bathroom. Imagine! Here is a proud, 110 pound, 5'2" woman who'd rather be dead than in a rest home telling me she's stepping in and out of her tub every day. Every day she puts herself at an unnecessary risk. She has plenty of financial resources, money is not an issue. Every day, as she ages, the risk increases.

I think part of the aging process is about still proving

1

our independence and youthfulness. From the time we're young, we are educated so we can be independent. We got our drivers licenses and jobs or careers. We moved out, had families, and tried to raise *them* to be independent. Now our children are grown and raising children to be independent. Now we have our own money and time and, "Nobody is going to tell me what to do."

I think you could have described my elderly parents as inflexible and fiercely independent. The synonyms could be stubborn and hardheaded. The "fountain of youth" myth has possessed every generation. I tell people that if I didn't own a mirror, I'd think I was twenty-five, not sixty. We see former President H.W. Bush I skydiving at eighty years old; we see cruise commercials with "gray hairs" dancing and playing till all hours of the night. There is a never ending onslaught of commercials to sell us products to keep us young and independent. The sure fact is that aging will continue to progress until we die. Regardless of what we may see or hear in the media, age marches on! Getting older is a terminal affair! The question is, "How are we going to best handle it?"

If you truly want to remain as healthy and independent as possible, you must concentrate on "what is," not what you would like for it to be. Be the best you can be for your age. If you are seventy-five, then be the best seventy-five year old you can be. Accept that you're not fifty. Be as active and youthful as any seventy-five year old can be, but understand that at seventy-five there are different perils than at fifty. At fifty, if you fall off a ladder cleaning out your gutters, it might not hurt you. If it does, you get fixed, take whatever time off is necessary and then go back to work. At seventy-five or eighty, you almost surely are injured. You get fixed, go both to physical and vocational rehab and, if you are lucky, you recover and go back home with help. Most likely you'll end up in a rest home with your family visiting you on Sundays.

As you think about it, our nation was founded on the principle of independence. We have a national holiday named for it, Independence Day. We fought a war to gain our independence and still, to this day, our Nation is involved in trying to spread the message of independence throughout the world. Why should adult children with aging parents be surprised that their parents want to stay in their home and be as independent as possible until their end?

There are several websites assessing when one's needs have changed and care is necessary. I believe in "thinking ahead of disaster." The earlier we start implementing preventive changes and improvements for our personal well-being and home safety, the longer we remain independent. The nationwide average annual cost for rest home care is $64,000 per person according to the Department of Health and Senior Services. Locally the average annual cost is over $45,000 per person. The majority of us will pay for this expense from our own funds. With the proper planning and forethought, we should be able to stay in our own homes for less money. It is far less expensive to prevent a fall than to treat the resulting injuries from a fall. Typically, people desire to remain in their homes as long as they are able.

2.
Learning To Accept Help: A Task For Seniors

A number of years ago, we would go out to eat with my daughter and her husband. I often picked up the check. Over time, I noticed that my daughter continually declined to go out with us. They visited us frequently, but our cherished restaurant time diminished. I asked my daughter why she was reluctant to go out to eat with us and her answer caused me to change my perspective on giving and receiving. I had always practiced the philosophy that "it is more blessed to give than receive." At the time, I was a General Manager of a steel company making a lot of money. My daughter and her husband were in their forming years and while making enough money, I assumed they needed every penny to survive. At this point, about paying for dinner, I was inflexible and fiercely independent. My daughter's answer to me was, "Dad, we love you very much and enjoy eating out with you, but we're doing okay and have our own money. We would like to be able to buy your dinner when we go out or pay for our own." Yes, it had become true, she truly wanted to be independent, not beholden even to her father. In a sense of fairness, if I may give to her, she also may give to me.

The aging point I make here is this: In my quest for continuing independence as I age, my inflexibility and fierce independence may actually drive my loved ones away. Even though I don't think I need any help, my loved ones may see it differently. Accepting their help may allow them to feel better and may actually strengthen our relationship. Truth is, if they are 50 and I'm 80, they probably have a better understanding of how to keep me in my home, not the rest home, than I do! No, I don't want to become dependent on my children. I do, however, want them to be close to me for the rest of my life. Hopefully, together, we'll get me to the end as peacefully and as happily as possible.

3.
The Journey With My Parents Begins

It was a typical fall day; cool, sunny with a slight breeze blowing the fall leaves. It was one of those days where you could just taste a bowl of homemade soup. I've always liked to cook and have developed a recipe for hamburger and cabbage soup. Today was the day it would hit the spot. When cooking, I have the habit of preparing a lot more than is practical. It was Sunday and I thought it would be a great day to see my parents.

Mom and Dad lived just outside of town on a place my grandmother had purchased in the mid 1950's. I spent a lot of time with my grandmother at this location and had a horse that I rode when I was eleven years old. At twelve, I helped an old carpenter, hired by my Dad, build a small horse barn. It still stands. My maternal grandmother passed away in the 1980's. My Mom and Dad moved to her home in the early 1990's. At this time, Mom and Dad were in their mid eighties and appeared to be very self-sufficient and safe in their home. Dad drove, kept a huge garden, cut wood for the stove, cared for his horse and walked two miles ever day. They were the picture of independence.

My Mom and Dad were then married for sixty-five years and living independently in a rural setting with adult children nearby. Dad was the epitome of a self-made business man. He had been reasonably successful based on working extremely hard, putting in long hours, and putting work above all else. In his generation, the most important way to care for his family was to be a good provider. He was from the Depression Era when men didn't cry and believed that sacrificing in favor of being a good provider was paramount. This era created men who had a hard time expressing love to their children or their feelings in general. His generation truly thought that being a strong, ethical and hardworking provider was their role. Many of this generation worked long, hard hours and were definitely viewed as the "head" of the household. This is probably a throwback to the hunter-gatherer time gone by.

Mom was a sweet elderly lady who had been the caring nurturing family member. She raised a family of four children, delivering kids to football, baseball, track and ballet. Many times she insulated us from Dad's moods. Looking back, the stress of working seven days a week, from daylight until dark or later, must have been enormous. Mom kept the books for the family business as well as all past and current tax, title, and other family documents. Even at this time, if it were a detail item, Mom was responsible. She was patient, kind and nurturing.

On this beautiful day I served up the cabbage beef soup. Both Mom and Dad were slight people, Mom about 110 pounds and 5 feet tall. Dad was 5'9" and weighed 139 pounds. Mom ate a bowl of soup while Dad ate three bowls. Now this was mid-afternoon and they told me they'd had a good lunch. As I thought about them on the way home, it occurred to me that Dad ate the soup not because he liked it but because he was hungry. I had siblings living near Mom and Dad and I asked them about my parents' nutritional habits. Their response was that my parents needed to do a better job of feeding and caring for themselves. My siblings' observations were that my parents need to buy more nutritious foods and prepare better balanced meals. They also needed to keep their house cleaner, stop driving, and change their clothes more often.

A few days later I prepared and took more food to my parents, enough for three or four main meals. I explained to them that I really liked to cook and this was some more stuff to try. I bought some frozen pizzas and other frozen prepared foods at the store and put them in my parents' freezer; foods they liked to eat that were very easy for them to prepare. I took them food I prepared on Sunday to last for three or four meals. I would trade dishes, new food for empty dishes.

In the beginning, my Dad would curse and complain that he didn't want to become dependent on his children. The food, however, was always eaten, and my parents appeared to be healthier. One Sunday afternoon when I arrived with food my Dad cussed and said, "By God, don't bring any more food. I'm not going to be dependent on my kids." My mother was a petite sweet little old woman who, with an angelic look, quietly said, "Honey, keep bringing the food."

As I took food to my parents, I began to notice other things in their home. It really wasn't kept as clean as it used to be. The mail would stack up on the table. Food in the refrigerator was spoiled or out of date. Dad really didn't drive as well as he used to, although he still drove at break-neck speeds. Simple tasks had become more difficult, bills were harder to understand, and they were becoming more confused when outside their home.

At Mom's current stage, she had become more frail and forgetful. Her memory was fading, yet her outlook was positive. You could tell that this union came from the era when behind every good, strong, successful man, there was a woman. In this case, and probably most, what the saying didn't say was that the woman was equally strong and successful in her own role. However, she quietly remained behind the limelight.

As elders, they had no social outlets to provide structure. In earlier years, Mom was involved in a Spanish club, attended church, and traveled with my sister. Now that she was elderly those activities stopped.

My parents had lived independently for all these many years. During this period, they went to the bank and

9

always went inside to have people contact. They also went to the store for groceries. Occasionally they went to the Chevrolet dealership to get their car serviced. It was apparent that their outings were their socialization. Dad was always telling jokes and Mom was his "straight man." If you saw them in these situations, it was reminiscent of "Burns and Allen". (If you're under forty-five, you probably need to Google George Burns and Gracie Allen, who were a married comedy team.) When you saw them, they seemed to be the perfect couple enjoying the perfect retirement.

One evening at 8:30, the phone rang! On the other end of the line was my father, who to me was one of the most dynamic, self-made, in-charge people I knew. Dad was in tears! My eighty-seven year old mother had fallen in their country home and Dad couldn't get her off the floor. My siblings, who lived in their area, were not available, so I hurried the fifteen miles into the country to help. I found Mom lying on her side in pain and unable to use her left arm. Struggling, my Dad and I were able to get Mom up and into a chair. At the hospital I learned that Mom had tried to break her fall with her left arm, resulting in a left shoulder fracture. Apparently, at Mom's age, this was not an unusual accident. After a short hospitalization, Mom was sent to a skilled nursing facility for continuing care.

At the time of this accident, Mom and Dad had been married sixty-five years. They had lived alone in the country for the past twenty years. A few years earlier, Mom had a minor stroke and the house was fitted with grab bars, hand rails and other items to make it safer. Mom and Dad seemed otherwise safe and able to function. They had been so fiercely independent that it took this accident to convince the family that they were no longer safe at home.

In watching my Dad visit with Mom as she recovered, the amount of separation, pain and grieving was enormous. There was pressure on Dad to move into assisted living with Mom. However, they had indicated in their advance directive their desire to remain in their home until their end. The family was now faced with how to care for them. How could we keep them safe and comfortable until their end? I phoned the State and found out that if they qualified for Medicaid, there were all sorts of services available for their care within their home. While not wealthy, they did have the resources to pay for services and were well above Medicaid guidelines. Since they would require no medical services, Medicare offered no coverage. I was faced with a problem that millions of adult children with aging parents are now facing.

In the years after Mom's fall, she became less mobile. Over time, if we took her out of the home, we had to use a wheelchair. I'll always treasure the memories of how much delight she received from her weekly visits to the hairdresser. She never got so old that she didn't want a little pampering. I think this helped her with her already positive attitude about life. She used to tell me that one of the nice things about growing old and losing her memory was that she could read the same book every week and enjoy it each time. When I was worried about her well-being, she would reassure me, saying she was "just a little old woman who had lived too long." I explained to them that, in their last years, the mission was to keep their bellies full and to keep them as safe and comfortable as possible. In her last year, she was in familiar surroundings with her husband of sixty-seven years. She had her dog, her cat, and her personal caregiver. Even at ninety she tried to get up and move unassisted. I'd warn her, "Mom, if you fall and break a hip, you might have to be put to sleep."

Midway through her ninetieth year, she passed peacefully in her own bed. No one thinks of death as a victory; though, my sister, who was at Mom's side when she passed, said it was exactly as Mom had wished. The lesson in this life story is as follows: We need to be objective in assessing what the actual current situation IS, not what we want it to be, hope or pray it could be, or the aging people want us to believe it to be.

4.
Seeing And Accepting "What Is"

There is a physics or reality at work in the aging process which cannot be overlooked. We can be in denial, we can be co-dependent, we can be enablers, we can hope, we can pray, but what we can't do is change the reality of a situation. We may be able to make the situation worse or improve it. However, we can't improve it unless we fairly and objectively assess and accept the reality of the situation. It is what it is!

I believe in what I call a "threshold theory." If life were air, we start out with an abundant supply, seemingly unending. As we develop, we adapt and use the air to sustain us and become accustomed to adequate levels. As we age, the available levels diminish so we continually adjust to diminished levels. Our adjustments are automatic. We unconsciously continue to adapt to our lives. When we are in our final years, the diminished supply begins to affect our ability to function. We continue to adjust and the supply continues to diminish. We ultimately reach a threshold that no longer will sustain us. We move to the other side. Since we are ever adapting, we don't notice the subtle changes we make as we adapt to reduced air supply. We keep narrowing our circles, activities, and energies to maintain some quality of life. Even though the process has been evolving since birth, there is a feeling that all at once our lives have changed. The aging process can almost seem like we were running and doing fine, then suddenly we hit a brick wall.

Mom and Dad had hit the wall. Mom was hospitalized, and Dad had a fear of going to the hospital. To him, it was a place to die. In his mind, Mom would die, or worse, be taken to a "nursing home." By this time in his life, his social skills were lacking. He was almost deaf and had dementia. I didn't recognize the dementia by name although my older brother correctly identified it. At this point, I only recognized Dad was easily confused, etc. I offered to take Dad to visit Mom which Dad eagerly accepted. I arrived during the noon hour to pick up Dad and inquired about lunch. He told me he had eaten and was ready to go see Mom. I asked what he'd eaten and his reply astonished me! He told me he ate a bowl of peanuts.

He was extremely health conscious. He ate raw garlic for heart health and, besides the peanuts, he had definitely eaten his garlic! We visited Mom and returned to his house. As I looked around with my eyes and mind open, I was overwhelmed by what I saw: Unopened mail stacked on the table, supposedly clean dishes that were dirty, spoiled food in the refrigerator, clutter, throw rugs that were trip and fall hazards. The rug in front of the wood burning stove had burns on it. There were scorched pots and pans and a dozen stray cats. I also saw this once independent man who was terrified that, after all these years, he may lose his sweetheart.

I'd been in their house on many occasions. Why had I not seen what I saw this day? The answer is obvious to me now. I always had seen my parents as independent, competent, capable people. Like many children, I still sought their advice on issues. I don't think it had occurred to me that someday they would become incapable of caring for themselves. As I looked around, I started to see a different picture.

5.
Different Siblings, Different Perspectives

My siblings, who were also seeing our parents aging process, had their own perspectives. This often occurs. They saw people who should do a better job of taking care of themselves. They saw an old man who shouldn't drive anymore. They saw a couple who should do a better job of meal preparation or buy prepared meals. They saw a totally dysfunctional setting, which they kept trying to make functional. Each time they arrived, there was dissention with Mom and Dad. They tried to hold them accountable and to get them to do better and change. Their analysis of the situation was it was dysfunctional and somehow Mom and Dad had to make it functional or go to a nursing home. They kept expecting to see our parents normal and functioning as they always had. This was a new scene and it was painful to accept the reality of our parents aging and decline.

I saw the same dysfunction as my siblings, although I saw it from a different perspective. I could see Mom and Dad were failing. I thought, "If they are hungry, I'll feed them." I started to bring food that I prepared, as well as frozen items they could prepare. I took the attitude that I shouldn't complain about their poor choices, I should help them choose.

I tried to help with the mail but, with the bulk being junk mail, it seemed to be destined to be table clutter. There is something about old people being afraid they'll throw something away that they should keep. I did, however, get

15

the bills or mail that needed some reply opened and in their hands. I helped Dad with the bills, etc. There was a lot of family pressure to stop Dad from driving. As I told you, they were in a rural setting and the closest store was seven miles away. I realized the demand for Dad to stop driving needed to be accompanied by an alternative solution. I found that Dad would let me take him to the bank or to the store or simply for a ride. The solution was, "If you don't want Dad to drive, take him where he needs to go. Don't take away his license; take away his need to drive."

When my siblings were there, they kept expecting to see our parents as normal and functioning as they always had. What I saw was my parents; two little old people who were mid-eighties doing the best they could. I saw a situation where they needed assistance, not condemnation. My siblings tried to see a situation they hoped would be; a situation they wanted it to be; a situation they prayed it could be. Sadly, it couldn't be. I saw a situation that was! When I drove up, I was never disappointed. The situation was as I expected it to be. I could make it worse, I could make it better; I just couldn't change it. I told my Mom and Dad that my sole goal was to keep them together; their bellies full, as peaceful and happy as they could be until their end. Over time and with the help and support of my siblings, we all accepted "what is" instead of what we would have preferred it to be.

Birth Order

There were multiple dynamics in my family as in every family. Birth order may impact these dynamics. I had two older brothers and a younger sister. I think if we analyze our perceptions of our upbringing, we often believe we were treated differently than our siblings. Raising my children tells me this is a true perception. The thing we don't consider is that time and circumstance change for all of us. If you are an only child, you have an entirely different set of circumstances to deal with.

Imagine how my parents must have felt when their first child was born. How excited, nervous, happy, apprehensive, and what great expectations they had! Many first born male children are named after their fathers. I'm sure there is the feeling that the first born will carry on the family tradition and inherit the role of head of the family. He is the chosen successor, the heir to the throne, the golden child. Imagine the pressures and expectations placed on the first born. Plus, there's exposure to the limelight of family, and to friends, neighbors, business associates, and anyone else we can tell. The second son is born a couple of years later. I assume there is a lot of fanfare and expectation but not as much nervousness. After all, we didn't kill the first one nor die ourselves; we can certainly manage another one. Now this child has to learn to be number two. No matter what, he can't be the first born. The first born will have to learn to share things as well as the attention. He also will continue to reinforce his position of heir apparent. The second son may be more competitive. He recognizes he can't be first and probably isn't last so he has to establish his place in the family. As the third is born, in this case me, the comments are focused on the delight of having a third child. There wasn't as many birthright expectations evidenced by years of hearing, "What a sweet child he is." In my case, there were four years in-between me and my brothers. They were close, sharing many of the same friends, competitions, etc. I was far enough back that I didn't fit in with them except maybe to be teased about being fat or something else. On the other hand, my brothers were always there to protect me from the bullies of childhood.

My mother took more of an active role raising me. She intervened with my brothers and kept some fairness in the family. My sister was born three years after I was and, boy, was she my mother's girl since Dad had his three boys.

Also, family economics change. Generally there isn't as much income for the earlier children. Family earnings increase so there is more money available and older children may see younger siblings get things the older children only dreamed of having.

We are who we are. When our parents start to become our responsibility, all of our upbringing and birth position comes into play. Your relationship with your parent will determine your original attitude toward that parent's care. If you were dominated, controlled, and always held to a higher standard, some may return that behavior. On the other hand, if you were the "sweet child," you may be more caring. It has to do with the expectations during your upbringing. It is harder for the first born, driven child to see his/her dynamic parent fail than it is for the "sweet child." As our parents age, all of our family dynamics are put in play: birth position, how we were treated, our expectations, our parent's expectations for us, and our expectations for each other.

It is very important as you become a potential caregiver to consider all the family dynamics. If you are lucky enough to be the responsible party and have siblings, not only will you have the responsibility for your aging parents, you also will have the stress of dealing with your siblings. My guess is, the greater number of siblings, the more disagreement there can be on how to care for the parent. It will be all right if you, as the caregiver, are able to understand why they feel as they feel. As the person responsible, you must always keep the goal in sight and not be swayed. Be understanding but don't waver from the best care plan for your parents.

6.
Different Emotional Baggage

I heard Ted Turner, who started CNN and owned the Atlanta Braves and all kinds of other stuff, say on TV one night, "You're born, you die; I'm just trying to fill the time in-between." In the time in-between, we accumulate a lot of baggage. I'm not a Social Worker, Psychologist, or Sooth-sayer, but it is obvious to me that the collection starts shortly after birth and doesn't end until we die. The way we were parented and the subsequent life-long relationships with our parents dramatically effect the way we view and handle our parents' aging and passing.

As we all know, baggage comes in many sizes and shapes; some good, some bad; some attractive, some ugly. In our life cycle, we continue to add and discard our bag-gage. Some children grow up in Norman Rockwell families. They honor thy father and mother (who are honorable), learn good values, are parented well, and pick up good childhood baggage. For those raised by loving parents who've earned a lifetime of respect, our grief at their decline and death may be devastating, tempered only by our gratitude for having had them and by our peace in knowing they no longer suffer. Helping them during those years may be difficult but it also can be a source of much love and meaning.

Some children are raised in homes of excess. This can be excess material things, being "spoiled rotten." Other excesses can be of discipline, strictness or religious beliefs, where parents show no confidence in their children. There also are children raised in abusive homes, alcoholic homes, impoverished homes or homes void of parenting skills. All of us pack our bags along whatever path we've been dealt. This greatly impacts how we deal with our parents aging and passing.

One thing we have in common is that, on average, children outlive their parents. Remember, our parents have their own bags which contain their own circumstances and obstacles when raising us, as well as how they were raised. They too may have suffered abuse and heartache. They often give us what they themselves were given. As they age and we age, we rearrange and collect all sorts of new baggage. Life seems to be a cycle. When you are born, you are totally dependent on others for your care and nurturing. You grow independent, have families, friends, and are in the prime of your life. As you age, the process generally reverses itself. You may be lucky and die before you become completely dependent again. Most people live long enough to need some degree of help to maintain their independence and quality of life. As we recognize that our parents or loved ones are beginning to need help, we realize there is baggage we've packed over time that we now have to deal with. Should we help? Can we help? Do they deserve help? How much help do they need? Am I willing to make this commitment based on how I've been treated? Will I reopen old emotional wounds?

Children whose baggage is from alcoholism, abuse, or neglect have probably figured out a coping method. Many times, keeping an appropriate distance or having no contact at all with the parent is the solution. That may be how you've emotionally survived. The question becomes, "What am I supposed to do?" The answer is, "You must do what is right for you!" You've been packing bags and you don't want to pack any more now. I think the best mental image to help you is, "How are *you* going to feel at the funeral? Are you going to be full of hostility and guilt? Are you going to be caught up in your old feelings? Are you at peace with your decisions?"

We are not responsible for other people's actions. We may react in certain ways based on our baggage or events in our lives. I'm not suggesting you are obligated to care for someone that totally abused you, beat you or whatever. I'm suggesting that you are ultimately responsible for your own actions. The cemetery is a place where you can either take on or leave baggage. If you are at peace with your decisions, you can leave a lot of accumulated baggage. If you are at the cemetery thinking of all the things you should have or could have done, you are picking up new bags that may be with you to your end.

I was brought up in a very loving household with a loving, caring, nurturing mother. As I've written, my father was a self made man with lots of baggage from his child-hood. His father died at an early age leaving his mother well off financially with three boys to raise. I don't think my father ever was able to cope with his Dad's death or the remarriage of his mother.

Then the Depression hit. The Depression left the family poor like many others. Dad had a fear of being broke and not being able to support his family. I always knew Dad loved me, however, he was the epitome of, "It's my way or the door way." He owned a service station and both of my older brothers and I worked there at one time or another. I started working at age 10. Wearing a uniform, I stood on a pop case and washed car windshields. Dad could be bet-ter described as a slave master rather than a father at work. He thought teaching us how to work and to be thorough, and frugal was his role. His language at work would make a sailor blush. He prided himself on being called "Scrooge" in public. Don't get me wrong, we had wonderful Christmas celebrations, charge accounts at the best stores, the latest in innovations (we had the first color TV and air conditioner in our block) and everything we could possibly need. When we were young, he took us to Florida during the Christmas break. We were the only kids in school with suntans in January. Otherwise, he worked.

Dad paid the house off in 1939 and prided himself on not having any debt till the day he died in 2004. As a young man, I worked for Dad. During the summer months, I literally worked eight days per week. Along with the station, Dad owned and operated a boat dock and concession on a local lake, which was open from daylight until dark seven days per week. Our service station was located just off a major interstate and was open twenty-four hours, seven days per week. The station never closed. I worked every day at the boat dock from daylight until dark. One night per week I worked at the station relieving the night shift attendant from dark to daylight. As soon as I was relieved at the station, I returned to work at the boat dock. Since this is my book, I claim this is working eight days per week. I worked for Dad until he fired me at age twenty. I was more of a "loose cannon" in those days. There was an incident that angered Dad and he fired me. A few hours later he phoned to make up and get me to return. I thought it over and decided that I wasn't going to conform to his demand. Therefore, I needed to work elsewhere. This decision turned out to be good for both of us. My father remained in the seven day workweek and continued to work seventy hours per week in his business until his retirement at age sevety.

I moved into the industrial field. My first job was at Paul Mueller Co. which paid $2.00 hour. Gosh! That was $80.00 a week, and I only had to work forty hours. Dad had been paying me $50 a week. He not only owned a twenty-four-hour service station but also the boat dock at Fellows Lake. I worked seven days a week in the summer at the dock and came in one night a week to let the night man off. Gosh!! $80 to work forty hours, who'd have thought it? Boy, was I getting ready to pack some new bags. In fairness to what Dad paid me, he also covered car and insurance expenses and protected me from debt at any cost.

As I married and started this new career and life style, it was totally different than Dad's. I entered the new world. Everything I owned was on credit. I had time off to be with my family and be somewhat caring and nurturing.

All my life, I was heavier than Dad wanted me to be, so I was always his fat child. My siblings were much more athletic. While they exercised, I cooked and ate. Most of my adult life, when I was around my father, he criticized me for either my weight or my debt or both.

When feeding my slightly built father, toward the end of his life, my sister would fix tofu and healthy foods. She had been a marathon runner and, to this day, observes a very healthy runners diet. I was always the most overweight of my siblings. My father's perception of me was that of a "fat child." After a few tofu meals, my Dad (at only 130 pounds) requested that I "keep bringing the food." Sometimes it is good to have a "fat child."

Neither Mom nor Dad had time to baby sit or to be grandparents to my children. We got together on major holidays; however, for the most part, the only way I could get along with them was to stay away. I want to make it perfectly clear that I loved my parents very much, and I know they loved me. We just didn't get along well together for any period of time.

As I began to help them, my children questioned me. They wanted to know why I would help since they believed Mom and Dad hadn't earned this type of treatment. This new responsibility brought up baggage from my children's past. It also reminded them of many hurtful things they had seen my parents do to me. Many of us are the type of people who never let others know that they emotionally hurt us. We show our independent faces and appear to be unscathed by the "you're too fat," "you can't manage money," or other hurtful comments from loved ones. There also are the guilting phrases we all hear: "You don't love me anymore." "Don't worry about me." "If something happens I'll just call the undertaker." "I've spent my whole life for you, and this is how you repay me," etc, etc.

My Mom would say to me, "I don't have time for your children; I'm too busy with your sister's." I don't know how many times I heard that one. Keep in mind, our children see us at home at times when we are the most vulnerable. They may hear us cuss or see us cry as we react to our loved ones. Our children pack this in their bags and, out of love for us, they bring it up when they see things that appear to be unfair. I remember the conversations with my adult children. I explained that I believe we are ultimately responsible for only our actions. How I handle situations is in my hands. I considered, "How am I going to feel at the funeral?" Later, my son and his wife remarked, "If we came across two little old people in the neighborhood we didn't know, we'd feed them." There is a difference. If they were strangers, we would have a different emotional involvement.

The question returns. "If a lot of bad things were packed in your bags, how do you act?" Maybe the answer for you is to treat them like strangers emotionally. Don't get hooked into the past, concentrate on the issue at hand.

A woman we'll call Rachel had many years of struggling with a hurtful, alcoholic parent. Rachel finally learned to refuse to accept unacceptable behavior. After many frustrating years, she refused to have contact until the parent sought sobriety. Once the parent was sober, Rachel was able to have superficial contact. When the parent became elderly and needed help, Rachel had several choices to make. Should she treat her parent as she was treated? Her parent was a responsible parent but had not treated her "nicely" as a child or as an adult. Rachel was not able to bring her parent into her home to personally provide care. She didn't trust the parent and refused to be "set up" for psychological trauma. She recognized that she had no control over her parent's actions. She did, however, have control over her actions. She determined that she would be responsible to see that the parent was cared for in a decent place. She visited and saw that the parent's bills were paid. To be true to herself, Rachel needed to be responsible and do the "right" thing. She also knew that, for her emotional health, she must be somewhat detached. When Rachel was faced with the bags she packed during a relationship with a dysfunctional parent, she took the appropriate action. By being responsible for her own actions, she didn't pack any new bags and was able to let some baggage go.

You're Still the Child!

I was visiting with a friend who is in the beginning stages of caring for aging parents. There are so many dynamics in play that it is difficult. The issues of how we age and how we were parented become acute. In this case, the parents are not only making poor personal care choices, they are still attempting to control the adult child.

During the conversation, my friend Julie related conversations about the parents' concern for how she drove. I believe they also were critical of other areas of her life even thought she was well over fifty. To the parents, Julie still was their dependent child. To the adult child, it was her parents who needed help and were deteriorating rapidly. It was obvious there wasn't going to be a lot my friend was going to be able to accomplish. I suggested that detachment was needed. Keep the focus of their well-being in mind and don't let your parents "hook" you.

I watched Dad manipulate my sister almost until the day he died. He continually evaluated her decisions and led her to believe that somehow he was more capable of making her decisions than she was. Mind you, this was a man who couldn't find his hedge trimmers or figure out what to eat. My sister has a masters degree and is a retired teacher. Her problem was that she always gave credence to Dad's input. It kind of reminds me of asking my twelve year old grandson for financial advice. It would be interesting to hear but not likely to be suited for my use. Emotionally they are still our parents and we expect (perhaps from habit) them to be wise and a valuable source of advice. Be careful here. My Dad, or Mom for that matter, couldn't program the VCR, use a cell phone or use a credit card. They couldn't even recognize a computer, didn't have a clue what the Internet was, and numerous other current things. They hadn't owed anybody any money since 1935 so they had no idea how credit worked.

I could never have bought a car or a house without the use of credit. I traveled for my job and couldn't get plane tickets, hotel rooms or car rentals without my American Express card. Dad couldn't understand any of this. He came through the Depression and lived a much different life than my sister or I. I learned a lot from Dad. However, the world changed and, at some point, it grew past him. He was great with horses and his garden and that advice was priceless. His advice on credit was worthless. He grew up in a cash based society whereas I grew up in a credit based society. Don't get me wrong, too much credit can break you.

My point here is, be careful of how much anguish you give yourself or your aging parents over their opinions. Things are changing and, by this time, you should be comfortable with your own decisions. Don't engage them in debate over something they aren't qualified to decide. Don't let them hook you. Detach and do what is right for them regardless of their attitude toward us. Love them if you can, respect them if they are respectful, but remember the roles are reversing. In some ways, neither of you want the roles to reverse, but over time the adult child becomes the stable, mature decision maker. For it to be otherwise invites disaster.

It is hard for me to write this. After all, I'm forecasting a future that none of us wants, and I don't want to die in the rest home either. I think that maybe I won't let my son or daughters read this book. I'm sure if I do, my words will be fed back to me.

As I write and reminisce about my journey, it seems like the end-of-life events I shared with parents had the perfect ending. First of all, it wasn't perfect. Second of all, it wasn't easy. It is possible, however.

Adult children who keep their parents home have to be able to handle all sorts of things and try not to put their own needs, feelings and emotions first. Believe me, on many days, we won't succeed. I guess that in some ways it was selfish of me because my greatest driving motive was how *I* was going to feel at their funerals. My parents were beneficiaries of that obsession.

We all have different experiences which influence how we cope with aging parents. My wife's father died when she was young so she missed having him as a parent. She and her mother had a troubled relationship; nevertheless, she was there for her mother and did the best she could until the end. She just never was able to be "warm and fuzzy" about it. She ensured care for her mother and kept her in acceptable living arrangements. Their relationship had been badly damaged over the years and it was no longer possible for my wife to be close to her mother. My wife was at the stage in her relationship with her mother whereby she had to protect herself. She couldn't emotionally afford to let her mother "hook" her as she had in the past. In a way, I believe my wife's actions far exceed mine.

I had a lot of trouble and turmoil with my parents over the years although I never doubted their love and devotion. In the end, you must do what is right for you and your aging parents. This is a difficult journey. Every step of the way is a challenge. The first and greatest challenge is convincing your aging parent to accept help. Not just from you, but help from anybody. I've said repeatedly and will say again, "Nobody easily gives up their independence!" We become more protective of our independence as we age yet we become less competent. We insist on making key decisions at a time in our lives when maybe we should be listening to others. It is sort of like when we were dependent children trying to grow and mature. There were times it was vital for us to listen to others.

I remember going through the cycle. When we are young and dependent, our parents are the smartest people in the world. In our late teen years, we become the smartest people in the world. At some point in our twenties, we start to recognize that our parents were smarter than we gave them credit. We spend the bulk of our lives living and learning and become wise elderly people and probably, on the inside, have returned to believing we are again the smartest people in the world. As our lives progress, we become less competent in certain areas. However, we are not conditioned to easily turn over control to our adult children. At the end of the cycle we are becoming more dependent, and our adult children are becoming more competent. I guess it is their turn to be the smartest people in the world. Our adult children better handle all this wisdom carefully. Their adult children will probably treat them similarly to how they treat us.

7.
Realistically Assessing Your Parents' Abilities

Realistically Assessing Our Abilities

It is very difficult to realistically assess a situation when we and our loved ones are emotionally involved. Before we assess our parents' situations, let's first look at us.

It is very important for us to fairly asses our abilities. I believe we all vastly overestimate our abilities, even when we are younger. This gets worse with age. I've said many times that if I didn't own a mirror I'd think I'm twenty-five, not sixty-two. I, however, do own a mirror and now see a potbellied, gray haired guy with glasses gazing back at me. Surely the mirror has it wrong, this can't be me!

I was married to a woman for thirty-four years who passed away at age fifty-five. I was fifty-six at the time and had not expected to enter the dating market. I actually hadn't had a "date" with another woman for thirty-five years and was terrified at the prospect. My sister Jane introduced me to Ann; the nicest, sweetest little woman one could ever hope to meet. On our second date she commented on what a "find" I was as a date. She was speaking about my character, my ability to stay in a long-term committed relationship, raise a family who loved me, and be a successful member of society, etc.

Apparently there are both male and female predators in the middle age dating market who really don't want or aren't able to settle down. They are forty-five or fifty and still "dating around." Ann was looking for someone stable for a long-term relationship and eventually mentioned that I was a possible candidate. Again, "You don't know what a 'find' you are in today's dating market." In my mind, "Wow, a fifty-six year old stud! What a man!" I saw myself just moments before as a dumpy, gray haired, little old man, and now "I'm a stud, wow!" You know what they say, "Beauty is in the eyes of the beholder."

As we continued our relationship, which ended up in marriage, I was able to go back and visit some of my youth. Even though we are similar ages, it was fun to re-kindle thoughts and ideas that I hadn't had for years. We went to the fair and rode the rides, traveled to beaches and played in the sand and ocean, took walks in the park, danced on Beal Street in Memphis and ate in the French Quarter. It was a form of a rebirth. I was young again, able to leap tall buildings in a single bound. You know, the entire BS. Wow, I thought I was as capable as I ever was.

We were staying at a hideaway resort on Bull Shoals Lake during our first summer together and were expecting my daughter to arrive for dinner. It was mid-afternoon and not a cloud in the sky. The water was warm, inviting, and so clear you could see twenty feet down. We were boat riding and enjoying the freshness and beauty of the lake. We were in an area where there was very little traffic and noticed there seemed to be no one else around. We were moving slowly in an area with giant beautiful bluffs. We were talking and reminiscing about the days of old when I mentioned that I'd never been "skinning dipping." (You know, jumping in the lake without any clothes on.) There was no one around, the lake was inviting and, after all, we were young again. What the hell, we thought, let's do it! Off came the bathing suits and into the water we went. It was great, exhilarating, and more fun than I ever expected it to be. It was wonderful; so peaceful, one with nature, everything's perfect, all natural! We spent thirty to forty-five minutes being kids again and had a great time.

It was getting close to time for my daughter to arrive so we thought we'd better get back into the boat, dress, and head for the dock. I brought a boat ladder for us to use in case we were not able to get back into the boat. However, I'd never had to use one in the past. After all, I'm a stud. I should be able to get back into the boat without the ladder. You guessed it, the ladder didn't work. There was no way to prop it where you could use it. Our boat was a short-sided bass boat and the ladder was long with nothing for it to rest against to make it work. We tried the ladder several times and it just didn't work. Oh well, I thought, I'll just hop in and help Ann out. Sure! I couldn't even come close to getting into the boat. Did I mention that I had a torn muscle in my left arm which I didn't have when I was twenty-five?

Now we are starting to panic a little. After all, how will we explain this if a boat comes by and we have to ask for help? My wife is a Licensed Clinic Social Worker with a Masters degree. She teaches college courses and doesn't have a blemish on her record. I'm not perfect; although, I am a member of two Chambers of Commerce, various committees, have been an elder in my church, and chaired many start-up committees including a huge area Character Education program, and operate my own business. At best, this is going to be terribly embarrassing. At worst, we will drown and leave people wondering just exactly what we were doing.

I decided to wedge myself between the ladder and the boat so Ann would be able to get up the ladder. Great idea! She started up the ladder (all one-hundred pounds of her) and as she tried, it forced me under water. Before she could get out, I had to move or drown. Since I'm writing this, you know I moved. When I moved, splash, there went her naked bottom back into the water. This would have been real funny except we're still not in the boat. After about the third try I said, "Sweetie, you've got to be quicker, you're

31

killing me here!" Finally, I was able to hold my breath long enough to allow her to get into the boat. We repositioned the boat closer to the bluff and I was able to crawl out and get in. What a relief! Safe at last!

This true story has two morals. One is, you should pursue life and live to the fullest; just park the boat on shore so you can easily get back in. The real point is to fairly, realistically, and truthfully evaluate your current abilities. Know your limitations, don't really become an "old fool" trying to be younger that you are. When I jumped naked into that beautiful water, I was twenty five. When I tried to get back into the boat, I was fifty-seven. My, how quickly we age!

Eleven Signs You or Your Aging Parent May Need Help!

The following contains eleven items compiled from multiple Internet lists plus personal comments to consider when assessing the situation of an aging loved one.

1. Mail is Piling Up: I remember visiting my parents' house before becoming their caregiver. They ate on TV tables or a dining table in their kitchen. Their formal dining table had become the place that accumulated the mail. My father received some dividend checks by mail and knew how to identify them. He had most of his bills automatically paid directly from his checking account. He did receive a few other bills in the mail. Dad was a product of the Depression Era and could not stand to owe anyone money. He paid his bills upon receipt. As they aged, I noticed the mail piling up on the table. If he received something that looked like a bill from a regular source, he paid it immediately. On occasion, he double paid for goods or services because his method of recording payments wasn't very good. Some items went unpaid because he didn't open them or recognize the sender. The vast volumes of junk mail went unopened, but he was afraid to throw it away in case it might contain something of importance. Periodically I'd sort through the mail and straighten the mess for him. I'd have to put the junk mail in a sack "just in case." The lack of organization, as well as the inability to distinguish meaningless mail, is a sign that our elders are having trouble with processing simple or multiple tasks. They also are easily persuaded by certain offers that play to their aging inabilities. Requests for money to get them closer to God, or to make a million dollars for a small investment, and ads for non-prescription drugs, etc., are real perils for them. Managing their checking accounts, paying bills and even performing simple everyday activities become more difficult as people age. This is an easy, obvious sign that your aging loved one may need some assistance.

2.   Clutter: In my booklet, "How Safe Is Your Senior's Home?", clutter is one of the safety issues that we address. It is also one of the easy-to-spot warning signs that something is going on with the elder. Some people lived in a cluttered house or environment from youth. If your elder loved one is one of these people, you need to promote change for safety's sake. Falls are the leading cause of death in people seventy-four or older. Tripping due to clutter is a hazard that can be reduced. If your elder was normally very neat, clutter is a sign of more trouble on the horizon. My Dad was a "neat freak" and even until the end didn't have a lot of clutter other than mail. My wife and I are in our early sixties and we already have to fight the clutter urge. You can go into older people's homes and see shrines to the past. Things may be in the same place as they were twenty-five years ago. However, placement of objects and furniture needs to be relative to our ages. For safety purposes, clutter needs to be removed and living spaces need to be reevaluated.

3.   Food and Nutrition: Check expiration dates on items in the refrigerator or on any other perishable items. Also, check the supply of available food that the elder person can actually prepare. As we age, we lose some cooking ability. Many older people won't throw anything out. My Depression Era father didn't believe in wasting anything. Boy, you should have seen what we threw out of his refrigerator and freezer!

We had an elderly client who only wanted to eat sweets. Because of health problems, she was allowed only a very limited amount of sweets. At her daughter's instruction, our caregiver limited the sweet intake and fed her nutritionally balanced meals. The daughter loved us; the mother hated us. The point is that we can become more childlike as we age and want to "fill up on sweets." Remember when your Mom told you that it wasn't good for you? Well, if we live long enough, we'll probably hear that again. Be sure the food supply is adequate, nutritional, before the expiration date, and something they can prepare.

My mother had difficulty swallowing. Her food preparation required ground meat dishes, casseroles, mashed potatoes and other easily swallowed foods. Be aware of special nutritional or dietary needs.

Do they seem to be losing weight? Are they well-nourished? We believe that well-nourished seniors who remain free from accidents are able to remain in their own homes indefinitely.

4. Pots and Pans: According to the National Fire Safety Council, Inc. "Kitchen cooking is the third leading cause of fire deaths and the leading cause of injury among seniors."

Look for burning or scorching on the bottoms of pots, pans and cooking utensils. It seems the older we become, the more we rely on habit, pattern, or sequence in our daily tasks.

I'm sixty-two and an insulin dependent diabetic. My bedtime routine is to take my nightly dose of insulin, use the bathroom, brush my teeth, set the alarm clock and go to bed.

This is a very structured routine and, if followed, keeps me from missing essential ongoing activities. I've noticed in my own behavior that if something happens to get me out of my pattern, I may overlook a step. If I use the bathroom and receive a phone call, I may forget to brush my teeth. If I use the bathroom and brush my teeth *before* I take my insulin, I may forget to take my insulin. When we get out of sequence during our routine, we often forget something.

I have routines for cooking like older people. If you have an item on the stove that does not require constant monitoring, it is easy to become distracted and forget it. I use reminders such as smoke detectors and buzzers to prevent this. As we age, neither our senses nor memories improve. We may not hear the buzzer or detector or smell the smoke. Our distraction may be watering the flowers outside while forgetting something we are cooking. The kitchen fire may be our first reminder! When you are visiting your parents, look at the bottoms of the pots and pans. If you see telltale scorching or burning signs, it is time for gentle intervention.

The following suggestions are from the National Fire Safety Council, Inc.

- Wear snug or short-sleeved clothing while cooking or roll up longer sleeves.
- Use oven mitts to protect hands and arms.
- Never leave cooking unattended, especially when frying.
- For a pan fire, turn off the burner and remove the pan if you can do so safely or smother the fire with a lid. Never carry a flaming pan to the sink. Never use water or baking soda. It could make the fire spread.
- Turn off the burner before picking up a pot. Be sure it is not too heavy.
- Let microwave cooked foods stand for 1-2 minutes before removing plastic wrap or lids and then lift the corner farthest away from you. Stir well and test before tasting.

Never use metal or aluminum in a microwave.

They offer these other kitchen burn safety tips:

- Locate towels and pot holders away from oven and stove.
- Keep the stove surfaces free of clutter and built-up grease.
- Turn pot handles inward on the stove.
- Use a timer as a reminder to turn off burners and the oven.
- Turn off all burners until you return if called away from the stove while cooking.
- Make sure the stove and burners are turned off before going to bed or leaving the house.

5.   Personal Hygiene: As I mentioned earlier, my Dad was a "neat freak." As he began to break down, this changed. He wore the same jeans indefinitely. It was like "pulling teeth" to get them washed. He thought the washer was hard on them. I bought him new jeans for Christmas and birthdays, which he stored for "later." You could count on seeing him in a soiled flannel shirt and those old jeans. He would be unshaven and his hair would get much longer than in his earlier years. While visiting with people who are going through the aging process with their parents, I found this to be a common problem. The parent is wearing the same clothing over and over. A general decline in personal hygiene is another sign that help is needed. Dad also refused to get decayed teeth properly treated which caused significant health problems. Personal hygiene problems can lead to unintended health consequences. Other causes of problems can be from physical difficulties with performing the tasks of laundry and bathing. It also can be a sign of giving up or depression. Whatever the reason, it is a sign for some intervention.

6. Missing Medical Appointments: This can be a simple transportation issue or, as in my Dad's case, a general distrust of medicine and doctors. When Dad was acutely ill, he would agree to see a doctor or have medical tests. When he was feeling better, he wouldn't do any preventive or follow up medical visits. The symptom was better, but the problem still was untreated. His teeth are the best example. He had a couple of teeth that needed to be pulled. They became infected which caused him excruciating pain. On multiple occasions his dentist prescribed antibiotic for the infection. The infection had to be treated prior to removing the diseased teeth. When the antibiotic worked, the toothache disappeared and, since he was no longer in pain, he wouldn't get the teeth pulled. My sister believes this actually accelerated his death. This story relates to behavior and diminished thinking that leads to missed appointments.

Transportation is another key issue. It is easier to fix if the elder is willing to go but no longer drives. Remember, we don't want to be a burden on our children or anyone else for that matter. The person may simply not know how to arrange for transportation. This can easily be rectified. You can take them or ensure they obtain alternative transportation such as Assisting Aging Parents provides.

Another issue concerns the aging parents who still drive to the stores and to appointments. Our Medical Centers and doctors' offices have become very complex. There is a high volume of traffic to negotiate entering and exiting parking lots, and these offices are frequently on busy thoroughfares. Older people can be confused, frightened, or simply no longer capable of negotiating these situations. This causes them to miss appointments which puts their overall health at risk. Just because they appear to have the necessary means and resources to get to the doctor doesn't mean they can. Missed medical appointments or problems getting there require some form of intervention.

7. Medication: Forgetting or improperly taking medications obviously will lead to unintended negative consequences. Seniors can be under-medicated or over-medicated. Either can cause an immediate death. Suddenly stopping certain medicines is extremely harmful. Be sure the medicines are clearly identified and have clear dosing instructions. Determine if your senior clearly and completely understands when and how to take their medicine. Is there a means to remind them daily? What is the system for organization? When caring for my parents, I used weekly pill cases. I filled AM and PM medication doses based on their doctor's instructions. I included over-the-counter medications and vitamins they regularly used. Each time I visited, I checked the pill cases to ensure the medicine was being taken.

8. Inappropriate Clothing or Behavior: Sometimes you see the elderly inappropriately dressed. They may wear too many or too few articles of clothing. How someone dresses may be an indication of needing some help or of a health change.

They may wear virtually no clothing in extreme cold or a lot of clothing in extreme heat. Either can be dangerous. They may become aggravated and aggressive toward those trying to help them. They may speak inappropriately in public about personal affairs. Dad, very publicly, bragged in a rural post office about the money he had. At the time, they lived in the country. The news continually reports about rural elderly people being robbed and murdered for their money. Bragging publicly is an open invitation to trouble especially for a vulnerable elderly couple. Other behaviors could include getting easily lost or confused about where they are, wandering off and not recognizing familiar people. These can be signs for intervention. Just because someone has dementia or Alzheimer's doesn't mean they can't remain at home. It means they require appropriate supervision and help.

9. Depression and Suicide: The incidence of suicide among those sixty-five and over is increasing. Statistics for 2002 list over 5,500 suicides in this group. Depression can lead to serious health problems and even suicide. Older people frequently feel isolated and alone. Feelings of despair, lack of energy, losing interest in something they always took pride in or enjoyed, crying, repeated phone calls at odd hours, not wanting to get up or get dressed, and loss of appetite can all be signs of a problem. Monitor the mood and temperament of the elder. Early intervention can be meaningful and helpful for both you and your loved one.

10. Home Safety: We provide a companion booklet of suggestions on senior home safety. When you visit, be observant. One of the key elements in maintaining independence is home safety! Areas to consider include lighting, handrails, electrical cords and the accessibility of storage, storage methods, nutrition and the organization and dispensing of medications. Check for trip hazards including stairs, rugs, pets, exit from the home, etc. Consider bathroom safety including grab bar, toilet seat height, water temperature, entrance and exit from shower and tub.

11. Cognitive Ability: As I mentioned earlier, we need to objectively assess their current situation. Their cognitive ability is fundamentally a very important part of the assessment. When we visit, we see only a "snapshot" of their abilities. It is critical that we see the whole picture. My Dad was the epitome of a "show dog." When he had an audience, he was witty and bright. He was able to name many plants, flowers, and vegetables. He recited Shakespeare. The "snapshot" evaluation was of a capable, functional senior. As I learned to pay attention to his daily living activities, I quickly learned his actual capabilities. He couldn't remember where he left his hedge trimmers or hose nozzle. His animals were overweight because he couldn't remember whether or not he had feed them, so he'd feed them again. He couldn't remember to give Mom her medicine or to take his. He continually failed to order prescriptions on time. When I took him to basketball games at the college near where he grew up, he became confused and terrified. He could find where he planted a tree as a youth but couldn't find his way home. Diminishing cognitive abilities seem to be a sure complication of aging.

The older we get, the harder it is for us to process simple tasks and make simple decisions. I was visiting with an eighty-four year old woman who had lost her husband. She apparently had some money available and her home was paid for. She indicated that she wanted to stay in her home, but her children wanted her to move to the town where they lived. She mentioned selling her home to produce money to be able to stay in our town in lieu of moving. I agree that she was faced with a dilemma that would be confusing for any of us. We didn't go into a lot of detail although the option of a reverse mortgage was mentioned. I think it was presented to her as being similar to selling your home without having to move. Again, this is somewhat complex for a generation that grew up during the Depression and feared debt. However, what I saw was, at the mention of another option (no matter how valid), this sweet little lady was obviously overwhelmed. She dropped her head into her hands as if to hide.

I noticed all the anxiety over the new prescription drug plan. As you look at this new plan it has to be better than the zero benefit which had previously been the case. All seniors get something, and the lower their income the better the benefit. This must be good for seniors, but there is a major problem. Too many choices! If there had been three options which were easy to understand, most seniors would have been on board at the outset. There must have been twenty-seven different options (this is a guess so don't start counting). There are so many options that some people

41

will not participate simply because of the confusion. The local senior centers are overwhelmed with explanations to seniors. There is no way to tell how many man-hours are being spent, and yet some will still not get on the program. Hopefully, it will be the ones who it would help the most.

Some of the fears I hear from seniors is the possibility of some type of means testing which would result in the evaluation of their property. Even thought they may have little or no income nor available cash, they own land, property, etc. that does have significant value. They are trying to protect these properties to be able to pass them on to their children.

Processing simple information is not limited to financial activities. I've been speaking in area Senior Centers, generally before the noon meal. Each one has a set routine. The tables are numbered and everyone has their own assigned table. We say the pledge, a lunch prayer, and then are sent to the serving line by table number. There are notices along the way reminiscent of grade school cafeteria days. As we age, we put many things on auto pilot. We operate on habit or routine. I've already noticed that there are things that I must do each day and it is important that I not forget them. I have a routine for things like taking medicine or brushing my teeth. You know, simple everyday things that we do at the same time and in the same manner day in and day out. Now, if I'm on the way to take my medicine and there is a distraction like the phone ringing or my wife asking me to get her something, I might forget to take my medications.

There are lots of jokes about the forgetfulness of older people and, as you know, all good humor is rooted in truth. The problem with this behavior as we age is that it can lead to disaster! Things that are routine and simple also may be essential for our well-being. I see some elderly folks that literally don't remember if they've eaten. More obvious concerns are pots, pans or other items left on the stove that could end up starting a fire. Also, garage doors or entryway doors left open and unattended allow easy access to the home for petty thieves. If medicine is not "taken as prescribed," it can actually be more harmful than beneficial.

As we age, we narrow our focus. On one hand, this is a strength. Generally, what we enjoy doing, we do very well. We all know some elderly individuals who are "web experts." They can navigate the Internet, download photos, e-mail photos of grandkids or family and use all sorts of computer technology. They can do searches for arthritis, diabetes, gout, bladder control or many other health interests. A friend spoke of an eighty-seven year old man who ran five Internet companies. I see former business people who have taken an interest in their yards or gardening. Every blade of grass is perfect; landscaping that could make an issue of Better Homes and Gardens; gardens that produce items that could be shown at regional or state fairs. We see women who have and still collect antiques and paintings, knit beautiful garments or make flower beds and arrangements that are perfect. We focus on what we enjoy and where we still can be productive.

If our family or friends take a "snapshot" of our abilities, doing what we do well, they may get the wrong picture. I reference a comment by a friend pertaining to an eighty-seven year old individual. This person has five Internet companies and is very high functioning. My friend made the statement, "This fellow is as good as he was at forty-seven." My thoughts on this are there is one of two possibilities concerning this evaluation. Either my friend has taken an incomplete or inaccurate snapshot, or the fellow wasn't very good forty years ago at forty-seven. I don't believe it is possible to be as good at eighty-seven as you were at forty-seven!

My Dad was the epitome of good health at ninety years old. He could walk two miles, cut his own wood, quote Shakespeare and he had a terrific garden. He also wore the same clothes for more than a week and many times needed a shave and a haircut. I wrote in earlier sections about his inability to eat a healthy diet and keep himself properly nourished. He had spoiled items in the refrigerator and cooked concoctions of things to keep from throwing them out. He cooked some beans in the same pan that contained his coffee grounds and other assorted items. Some chefs might think this a creation. However I don't think it will catch on.

When you are dealing with the elderly, it is important that you see the entire picture, not just the snapshot. I believe that we *so* don't want to grow old that we want to see our parents as being younger and more capable than they really are. We must be able to see the whole picture. We must be prepared to manage a situation in its entirety or we may doom our parents to a life and death they dread. If our parents don't want to be a burden, we must think ahead of their needs and see their entire picture. We must be able to anticipate actions they may take that could cause them harm.

I watch the fights over taking someone's driver's license away. Our driver's license is our symbol of freedom. It is our sense of independence and who we still want to believe we are. Losing the ability to drive is certainly one of the most traumatic occurrences in our aging process. I believe that instead of taking away our parent's driver's license, we should take away their need to drive. If you take them places and anticipate where they may need to go, they may actually stop wanting to drive. Don't take away their license; take away their need to drive.

When you visit, pay attention to what you hear as well as see. Do they know what day, week, month and year it is? Do they forget names of relatives, friends or other familiar people? How aware are they of their surroundings? My Dad could misplace something within the room. He lost his glasses when they were on the table beside him. He left a desk drawer open. Upon return from a short ride, he thought the house had been burglarized because the drawer was open. Although there was cash in plain sight on the table, he thought someone had broken in and looked in his drawer. Pay attention to the things that confuse them or the things they forget. It can lead to what I call "invisible help." You can anticipate their needs and fulfill them ahead of time. They don't notice because you've already addressed an issue that would otherwise be difficult for them. For example, when I discovered my parents' nutritional problems, I made a casserole or meat loaf and mashed potatoes and left it for them. They were capable of warming things in the microwave. I'd leave frozen dinner items from our local Sam's Club, which they could microwave. As I visited, I'd see how much was left and replenished the food. They were still choosing and preparing their meals. I just insured the availability of nutritionally balanced choices and items they could now prepare (microwave and put on a plate). For their sake, recognize their true cognitive abilities and don't criticize them. They're not going to be able to make it better. You can make it better by accepting their situation. Don't criticize, condemn, or complain. Help them do the best they can. After all, it will happen to us if we live long enough.

When we visit our aging parents or friends or relatives, we should be social and observant as well. The quality of life for both our elderly loved ones and ourselves is much improved if we intervene at the appropriate time. We are not there to take over, we are there to assist. Nobody wants to become dependent, especially those who have been vital, dynamic people throughout their lives. Don't rob them of their dignity. Learn to assess the situation and then you can gently and compassionately create positive, proactive and preventive changes which are in the best interests of our elders.

45

The Quick List

1. Mail is Piling Up
2. Clutter
3. Food and Nutrition
4. Pots and Pans
5. Personal Hygiene
6. Missing Medical Appointments
7. Medication
8. Inappropriate Clothing or Behavior
9. Depression and Suicide
10. Home Safety
11. Cognitive Ability

At Assisting Aging Parents, we feel passionate about how our population ages. We are actively involved in analyzing and assessing the current situation and promoting positive changes for the future. It is our belief that the current model for viewing and working with aging issues is "reactive."

The best illustration is that the predominant providers of home care are health care providers. While medical care is essential, it represents only a small amount of the time spent on home care. The vast majority of home care is assistance with daily living activities. The model needs to become consumer driven, proactive and preventive. Our company employs a full time Licensed Nursing Home Administrator as a Professional Care Manager to provide comprehensive in-home evaluations. While there is a fee for this service, our recommendations are designed to best serve the senior in the most compassionate, affordable method. We provide information about services that best meet the senior's needs, whether provided by our agency or someone else.

8.
Senior Home Safety

It's easier, cheaper, and causes less pain to prevent an accident rather than treat the results of an accident.

During a recent visit to the doctor, I read a pamphlet published by the National Fire Safety Council, Inc., provided locally by the Springfield Missouri Fire Department, entitled "Safe Seniors." The Springfield Fire Department provides free residential safety surveys for anyone residing within the city. Residents must request the survey. This program may be available in your area. I recommend checking with your local fire department and using this service. I've referenced their publication in my cooking safety section.

To prevent falls, you need to make sure that there are not things in the home that can cause a fall. My company, Assisting Aging Parents, uses a Home Safety Checklist that is a compilation of many experts' advice plus some of our own. Now that we have cyber space, it is pretty hard to figure out whether you're having an original thought or read it somewhere on the Internet. I'm going to go over our list and add some comments. While I believe that these comments are my own, I'm old enough that there is no telling why I'm going to say what I'm going to say. Flip Wilson, the now dearly departed, hilarious black comedian from my era used to say, "The Devil made me do it!" Well, I'm not going to give the devil his due, I'm taking credit for this, and if you think you've heard it before, it's because it is all based on logic.

Lighting: Make sure an elderly person's lighting, both overhead lights and lamps, is bright enough to see. Put a night light in the area between the bed and bathroom. Place a lamp close to the bed where it is easy to reach. Make sure outside walkways and driveways are well lit. This isn't rocket science, it just makes sense. After all, the older we get, the worse the impact of a fall is.

There is a slight problem with this thought. My Dad was so thrifty that he wouldn't leave the lights on. Hell, he would rather bounce around the house in the dark than spend the two cents it took to keep lights on. As I think about it, he couldn't find his glasses in the daytime much less in the dark. The average annual cost per person for a rest home, according to the Department of Health and Human Services, nationwide is $64,000 per person. Is saving two cents worth that risk?

One of the things we need to be observant about while visiting grandma is the lighting and whether she leaves it on or not. It won't do any good to follow the advice on the list if grandma won't leave the light on. I believe I should have used the "glow in the dark stuff" they line airliner aisles with for my folks to find the bathroom at night. I'm trying to make this a little silly. However, it really is quite simple; be sure there is adequate lighting and continue to instruct your elderly loved one about the dangers of falling.

Area Rugs: Speaking of falling, if we put hurdles in lieu of area rugs in front of our elderly loved ones, they would at least recognize the peril. Anything that can move, that isn't bolted down, could cause them to lose their footing. I hadn't thought much about this except I do remember the night my Mom fell. I went to their home to help her up. Dad couldn't get her up and it turned out she had broken her shoulder in the fall. Now that I look back, she was partly on a throw rug located by their free-standing fireplace. I don't know if that was why she fell. I know that I should have removed it as an obstacle. The bright side is that if she hadn't fallen, broken her shoulder, ended up in skilled nursing, cried to come home and gotten me to be her caregiver, I wouldn't be as passionate about these issues as I am!

When I speak about fall hazards, I usually poke a little fun at cats. Is seems that a lot of older people have cats. I now have my first cat. I've been a dog man all my life; although, the cat's a pretty good friend. After all, our black lab Carson loves the cat. They're best buddies. It seems that cats have an annoying habit of getting under your feet. My cat is always just right there in the midst of my stride. I've had numerous vascular surgeries on my legs. Each time I come home, I have to be particularly careful to keep from falling. When you have staples in both legs from your ankles to your groin, walking is no simple matter. The last thing I want to see is my cat flipping his tail right in front of me. Well, if you're 87, it is equally dangerous. I'm not sure what I'm proposing here, surely not shooting the cat. Small pets can be trip hazards. Larger pets can actually knock an older person over. I am suggesting that when you're looking at throw rugs, there are also other obstacles to consider. The elderly do very well with pets, but we do need to ask them to "watch out" for the cat!

Carpet: Remove any bumps, raised edges, or other high places in their carpet. The carpet must be in acceptable condition for people who have difficulty picking up their feet. It seems, as a lot of us age, we shuffle our feet. Please pay attention while in your elderly loved one's home to the condition of any walking surfaces. For them, a simple fall can ultimately be fatal.

Non-Carpeted Floors: Do not wax or otherwise make them slick. Wipe up spills immediately.

Electrical Cords: Coil or tape cords and wires next to the walls to prevent falls or have an electrician put in additional outlets. There is an outlet in my kitchen with two spaces. I have plugged-in devices, which allow me to plug three cords into each space. Yes, six items run from one outlet. If the microwave is operating and I try to open a can, it blows a breaker. This can't be good. I'm only sixty-two. I may set an old age record of plugging in things if I don't burn my house down first. On the desk where my home laptop is located, I have so many cords strewn that when I move the chair to sit down at the desk, drawer comes open. Again, at sixty-two, it seems convenient to me, not dangerous. I'm sure the older I get, the less aware I'll be of these types of hazards although falling will become more critical. My wife thinks that a house fire, caused by overloaded cords, while we are asleep is more dangerous. We have smoke alarms to wake us up in case of a fire. There is no alarm on a poorly placed cord to prevent it from tripping me. Look around your parents' home and see if you can help.

Clutter: Remove clutter from floors, stairs and outside steps. Move furniture to allow a clear path for walking. This is pretty simple and straightforward except that, as we age, we don't want to throw anything away and if it's not under our feet, we're afraid that we'll lose it.

I once lived in a home with a large kitchen. I'm not a very tall guy so I kept a small step-ladder propped against a butcher block in the kitchen. When I became "single," I noticed that the ladder was gone. I discovered it in the garage and moved it back to its rightful place. You did have to walk around it and sometimes it would fall, hitting your ankle or another body part. It was nothing too serious but somehow annoying to someone. A few days later, it was back in the garage. I moved it back to its rightful place once again. Finally, my daughter Christy told me that she was moving it because it didn't belong in my path in the kitchen.

Christy indicated that this was for my own good. She and I had a different perspective. Her husband is nine inches taller than me and can easily reach things on top shelves. I can't! Truthfully, at my age, I shouldn't be putting things up high that I rarely use. I now store the stool in a safe and convenient location. The idea, to have something close just in case you may someday need it, could cause the fall that sends you to the nursing home. My wife came up with the phrase, "Go to the home 'cause of a broken hip, or prevent the fall and save the trip." Kind of clever, isn't it?

Stairs and Steps: Have railings on both sides of indoor and outdoor stairs. Be sure they are sturdy enough to hold someone. Fix loose or uneven steps. Have steps and stairwells brightly lit and clearly mark where stairs begin and end. Either paint stairs and steps different colors or use brightly covered tape. Put on-off light switches at the top and bottom of the stairs. Make sure the carpet is firmly attached to every step or remove the carpet and attach non-slip treads on the stairs. The reoccurring theme here, in case you're still missing it, is a fall ultimately can be fatal for an elderly person. My Mom fell and broke her shoulder. Due to the fall, she spent a week in the hospital and three months in a skilled nursing facility. The owner and Social Worker at the skilled nursing facility tried everything they knew to keep her there and get Dad to stay as well. I used to tease Mom (who had been around horses for years) about falling. Since she refused to be aware of the risk, I'd tell her, "Mom, if you fall and break a hip, I'm just going to have to put you to sleep." If you look at the possibilities of many elderly people returning to normal activities or going back home after breaking a hip, you'd probably find they have two chances; slim and none!

Storage: Store heavy items on lower shelves and lighter items on higher shelves. Also, items that are seldom used should be stored higher or further back in storage. Store frequently used items in easy-to-reach, center spaces. Have heavy soup or vegetable cans, etc., at eye level. Be sure, if a step stool is used, it has a bar to hold onto and a non-slip surface to step on. Never use a chair as a stool. As you survey the elder's house, check for ease of movement and be sure the storage of all items is easy for them to access. Not just the kitchen items but laundry, clothing and even gardening items need to be easily accessed. Insure that it is possible to get a good grip when picking up heavier objects. Also, keep light bulbs changed and anticipate maintaining gutters, washing windows, etc. which might pose a risk to the elderly. If you do these chores first, your elders are less likely to try dangerous chores themselves.

Water Heater, Toilet, Shower, and Bath: Make sure the water heater temperature is adjusted to be adequately warm without scalding. Either add a special toilet seat to make it higher or you may want to get a toilet that is higher. Install support bars around the area.

Shower and/or Bath: Use a non-slip mat on the floor. Install grab bars. Keep bathing products near where they are used and in easy-to-handle containers. For the tub, use a plug with a chain attached in order to safely unplug it. Fill the tub half full. Consider using a bath/shower chair and a shower head you can hold in your hand. I recommend removing the tub and replacing it with a shower with grab bars, seat, etc. already installed. A shower has a much smaller threshold to step over. If an additional seat is helpful, it is easy to move in and out plus easy to maintain. It really isn't funny when an older person is having difficulty getting up and down on the toilet or in and out of the tub or shower.

I spoke with an older friend who had been a caregiver for his elderly female friend. She didn't answer her door or phone for an unexpectedly long period of time at the retirement center where she lived. Friends noticed that she wasn't at dinner nor at breakfast the next morning. When the facility's cleaning staff opened her apartment, they discovered her, naked, wedged between the stool and tub, unable to get up. She was conscious and responsive, however she had lost her bowel and bladder control so was quite a mess. Apparently she had lain in this position more than twelve hours. (So much for the fallen and I can't get up device lying on the dresser.) The staff couldn't free her nor could my friend so emergency workers removed her. She was badly bruised and extremely embarrassed by this situation but otherwise not seriously injured.

Doors, door handles: Make sure doors can easily be unlocked from the outside if needed, as well as using a lock that is easy for the person on the inside. Consider changing from door knobs to lever-type handles for ease of access. Keep doorways and walking areas clean and clear of clutter, etc. so there is no trip hazard. Once again, it is important that all entrances and exits be well lighted for ease of entering and exiting the room or building.

There is an exception to the lock rule. If you are managing a person with Alzheimer's who has a tendency to wander off and get lost, place simple locks high enough to prevent them from leaving when not observed. This was suggested to a family caring for a loved one with Alzheimer's. Before they had an opportunity to implement this recommendation, their mother wandered out, fell and broke her neck. What heartbreak!

Medicine Organization: Death rates from accidental poisoning increase as we age. Identification, expiration dates, quantities, and dosing instructions must be visible and easy to understand. A regular reminder routine should be established to insure proper dosing. As I was monitoring my parents' situation, I used weekly pill case dispensers. I filled each day, both AM and PM doses, as instructed by our family physician. This allowed ample time for refills as they used their medications. I instructed our full-time caregiver to gently offer the medications or remind them to take it. Each time I visited, I checked the dispensers to see if the medications had been taken. Dad didn't like how he perceived a certain medication effected Mom. He thought it made her sleepy when he wanted her company. Thus, from time to time, he withheld the dose. When this occurred, the medication remained in the dispenser so it was easy to tell he was withholding the proper dosage.

Reference Materials

I am adding information on aging issues I've gathered from the Internet. I believe that we need to know as much as we can. Hopefully some of the links or numbers will be helpful for you. I know my office has spent many research hours on this issue and we continue to learn every day.

Visit http://www.feddesk.com/freehandbooks/1014-4.pdf to access the following information which begins on page seven of the handbook. I'm reprinting what I've downloaded from this link for your information. As you read the articles, I add comments from my observations after each section:

Aging Parents and Adult Children Together (A/PACT)

MAKING THE HOME SENIOR-FRIENDLY

(Third in a 10-part series)

Your parents are healthy and living in their home, but you worry about the danger of falls and other household injuries. What if one of them becomes ill or disabled? How would they manage? What can you do now to improve their safety and comfort or mitigate any possible injury?

It's wise to address concerns about your parents' safety and comfort in their home before a problem arises. Your parents probably share your concerns. Great strides have been made in designing and retrofitting public and private spaces to allow greater freedom and access for people with limitations and disabilities. These elements also can be used to enhance a home and eliminate safety hazards.

Evaluating your parents' home begins with a general safety check. Use this checklist to identify problem areas:

Throughout the home

- Are handrails securely fastened on both sides of all stairways?
- Are all areas, including stairways, well lit? Are switches easy to operate?
- Do outside lights illuminate entrances and exits?
- Is a telephone accessible at all times? You may want to suggest a cordless telephone with charger.
- Are outside doors protected by security locks that can be easily operated?
- Are smoke detectors and carbon monoxide detectors strategically located?
- Are batteries replaced on a regular basis?
- Are floors and stairs kept free of cords and loose objects?

Bathroom

- Is safety equipment properly installed? The basics are grab bars for the tub, shower and near the toilet.
- Do the tub and shower have non-slip surfaces?
- Is the hot water heater set to prevent scalding?
- Can you remove tripping hazards, such as cords and throw rugs?
- Is there a night light?

Bedroom

- Is there a sturdy bedside table with a non-tip lamp and space for eyeglasses?
- Does furniture placement allow a clear path between the bathroom and bedroom?
- Do rugs have non-slip backing?
- Is there a comfortable chair with arms for rest or comfort when dressing?

Kitchen

- Can frequently used items be reached without using a chair or stool?
- Is a fire extinguisher within easy reach of the stove?
- Is there a work area where a person can sit while preparing food?

Simple improvements identified through the checklist are inexpensive, barely affect the appearance of the home, and can make all the difference in an aging person's ability to continue living at home.

For older people with health problems, a home evaluation by an occupational therapist also can be helpful. This health professional can identify ways to improve home safety, arrange resources and modify the environment to compensate for specific disabilities. For example, home improvements for someone with severe arthritis could include installing lever-action faucets in sinks and tubs, replacing door knobs with lever handles, equipping the kitchen with an under-cabinet jar opener and electric can opener and replacing knobs or small handles on cupboards and drawers with larger "C" handles. Similarly, an avid gardener with knee or hip problems could continue gardening by having raised plant beds installed that can be reached from a standing or sitting position.

While some improvements can be done by the homeowner, others, such as a wheelchair ramp, may require a builder or contractor.

For More Information

The American Occupational Therapy Association
4720 Montgomery Lane
Bethesda, MD 20824-1220
(800) 668-8255 or (301) 652-2682; fax: (301) 652-7711
www.aota.org
The AOTA has information on: home safety for people with health problems, including Alzheimer's disease, adapting homes for older people, driver safety, and locating occupational therapy resources.

National Association of Area Agencies on Aging
1112 16th Street NW, Suite 100
Washington, DC 20036
(202) 296-8130
www.ncoa.org/lcao/member/naaaa.htm
NAAAA provides information on locating community resources for older adults.

Alzheimer's Association National Headquarters
919 North Michigan Avenue, Suite 1000
Chicago, IL 60611
(800) 272-3900
www.alz.org

American Association of Retired Persons
601 E Street, NW
Washington, DC 20049
www.aarp.org/programs/connect/orderform.htm
AARP pamphlets include, Home Modification: Independent Living Kit, Stock No. D16427; DoAble Renewable Home, Stock No. D12470; and Consumer Tipsheet: Home Modification, Stock No. D16236. Refer to the stock numbers when ordering.

Prepared by the American Occupational Therapy Association

Eric's Comments

"Making the Home More Senior Friendly" provides excellent advice. I've already written about Assisting Aging Parents' home evaluations. As we age, we can keep these things in mind for our own homes. My wife and I added-on a bathroom/utility addition with wheelchair access door spacing and a large shower with space for a seat, in lieu of a tub. Statistics indicate preventable accidents are a leading cause of admissions to nursing homes or deaths for seniors.

9.
Limitations Of "I've Fallen And Can't Get Up" Devices

There are devices for the elderly to activate if they've fallen and can't get up. We recognize that, while these are essential devices, they don't work unless worn. Also, in the case of blackouts, they offer no help. These devices, however, seem to be symbolic of how we currently view services for our aging population. Predominantly services are "reactive" and focus on taking action after something bad has happened. They often focus on the elderly who are poor or economically disadvantaged.

In our area, 7.5 % of citizens sixty-five and over are at or below poverty, according to the Missouri Senior Report released in 2006. That means there are 92.5% of senior citizens above the poverty level. The average household income of senior households reported for 2000 was $39,821. Currently the focus is on the 7.5% minority and driven by health care, hospice, "I've fallen and can't get up" devices, fraud reporting lines and elder abuse reporting lines. While all this is needed and necessary, all of these entities are "reacting" to elder care issues.

The "falling" devices are similar to your smoke detector. The smoke detector does a good job of telling you that your house is on fire. It doesn't do anything to prevent house fires. Society needs to change the elder care model to be "proactive and preventive" to help our seniors remain at home and be independent, hopefully until their death.

I am quoting from an ad on the back page of the

AARP Bulletin, April 2007: "My Mother does not want to go to a retirement home. My solution: I got her Life Alert, which gives her personal protection for medical, fire and intrusion emergencies, even when she cannot reach a telephone. She can keep on living at home, independently." It continues: "Coincidentally, I am very familiar with Life Alert. I live alone too. I used to get scared at night from every strange noise. I subscribed to Life Alert and one press of the waterproof pendant will get me immediate help 24/7, in the event of intrusion or other emergencies. I no longer feel scared." In a bold box they say, "In 20 years, Life Alert has never failed to chase away an intruder."

I want to point out that I don't have anything against Life Alert or any other device of this nature. I think these are worthwhile devices though very limited in their actual importance for senior safety. Prevention is always the number one safety tool. These devices, if worn and used properly, can only alert us to an event that has occurred. I joke that these services are the first to know you're going to the nursing home because of a fall. I hear of cases where the person falls from a "blackout" or some other reason, which makes it improbable to activate it. Or people leave it off to bathe and can't reach it when they fall.

My fear is that there is a false sense of security created by the way these devices are advertised. I was speaking with folks at a local retirement living facility. A very frail lady using a walker stopped to visit. She told me she had fallen a number of times and been injured. I was giving her some home safety tips and she interjected, "Oh, I'm safe now, I have 'xyz' device and it keeps me safe."

What a crock. To me, she had been seriously misled. It is a device to notify, not prevent. I've used the term before. It is similar to a fire detector that tells you your house is on fire. It doesn't help with fire prevention. Granted, the smoke detector may keep you from dying in the fire, but your house still burns down. Similarly, you may not die from a fall; you may just be in the nursing home for a long time.

Now let's address protection from intrusion. I live in Springfield Missouri. This is the epitome of mid-America. We are a centrally located, average community. Our metro area is about 450,000 and our overall trade area is approximately 1,000,000 people.

I looked at the response time for the local police and fire departments. The average minutes for a first responder to arrive from the Fire Department, reported for 2006, was 6 minutes for 80% of the calls. (I assume longer for the other 20%.) In 2005, it took the Police Department 8.73 minutes to respond for a priority one call.

Again, this type of advertising appealing to the elderly is creating a false sense of safety. I'm sure locally that if you are a thief, you know you have well over 5 minutes to break in, steal what you want and get out before the police arrive. I can just see it now. An eighty-nine year old, 110 pound grandma, threatening an intruder with her Life Alert. What's she going to hope for? The intruder choking on the button! Punch the button and now you have an additional emergency responder to deal with. Call me crazy, but calling 911 isn't that difficult if you are able to do everything else for yourself and you carry a cell phone or sleep by a phone. Again, I give them some credit for the fall notification... but... intruders? To quote one of my favorite authors and TV guys John Stossel, "Give Me a Break."

10.
Community Based Services

More information from the A/PACT handbook follows:

Aging Parents and Adult Children Together (A/PACT)

COMMUNITY-BASED SERVICES

(Last in a 10-part series)

As the elderly population grows, so, too, do community services for older people. Services may be provided by government, non-profit or for-profit organizations. Urban and suburban residents usually have a broader range of services than people who live in rural areas; the quality of services also can vary among communities. However, anywhere an elder lives, services of some sort are likely to be available.

You generally can count on community *senior centers* or local *community centers* to offer companionship. That's in addition to other services, including classes, recreational opportunities, travel, volunteer opportunities, flu shots and meals. Often, senior centers are the heart of activities for older people and a good resource for additional information.

Many communities offer *transportation services* for visits to the doctor, grocery store or senior center. Trips may be limited, though, and sometimes, transportation services are available only to those within certain income levels.

Community groups may sponsor *friendly visitors* or *companions* programs, where volunteers make scheduled visits to isolated seniors in their homes. There also are t*elephone reassurance* programs: volunteers call people to chat or check on their well-being.

A number of *home maintenance and repair* services specialize in installing devices that help older people better manage in their homes.

Older people who are homebound may get *meal delivery* through Meals-on-Wheels programs or private food service businesses. *Chore/personal care services* can be arranged to provide help with routine homemaking tasks, such as cooking and cleaning, or for activities like bathing and dressing.

Some public utilities and the U.S. Postal Service offer *gatekeeper/home observation* programs, in which service people who visit the home regularly are trained to notice anything unusual or any indication of need and report it for investigation and action.

Other services that may be available include *home health care, adult day programs* and *respite care*, which is designed to give caregivers a break from their responsibilities.

The Eldercare Locator Service — a nationwide, toll-free assistance directory sponsored by the National Association of Area Agencies on Aging — is a good place to start looking for services. Call (800) 677-1116. They'll give you the names of local organizations that offer legal, financial, health-care and other services for the older adults. The Locator is particularly useful if you're trying to provide care from a distance and don't know what services are available in another community. The service operates from 9 a.m. to 8 p.m., EST, Monday through Friday. Or visit them on the Internet at *www.ageinfo.org/elderloc.*

The U.S. Administration on Aging also has useful information for families. Call (202) 619-0724, or visit *www.aoa. dhhs.gov.* The government section (blue pages) of the telephone directory lists the local area agency on aging — sometimes called the City or County Office on Aging, Council on Aging or Office of Elder Affairs. Also check with the local health department, library, hospital and Department of Veterans Affairs.

For More Information

Age Pages
National Institute on Aging
P.O. Box 8057
Gaithersburg, MD 20898-8057
(800) 222-2225
www.nih.gov/nia

Alzheimer's Association
919 North Michigan Avenue
Suite 100
Chicago, IL 60611-1676
(800) 272-3900
www.alz.org

American Association of Homes and Services for the Aging
901 E Street, NW
Washington, DC 20004-2937
(202) 783-2242
www.aahsa.org

National Association for Home Care
228 Seventh Street, SE
Washington, DC 20003
(202) 547-7424
www.nahc.org

National Council on Aging
409 Third Street, SW
Suite 200
Washington, DC 20024
(202) 479-1200
www.ncoa.org

National Meals on Wheels Foundation
2675 44th Street SW, No. 305
Grand Rapids, MI 49509
(800) 999-6262

Prepared by the Federal Trade Commission and AARP

Eric's Comments

Within each community, there are unique services offered to the aging population. In my area, the company we created is one of multiple options for seniors. We are starting a support group for adult children with aging parents so we can better support and educate these children or care-givers about the journey they are about to take. We believe that some people end up in skilled nursing or rest home care through actions that were avoidable or preventable.

The most important support system is family, friends and other relatives who have some contact with the seniors. We shouldn't abandon our seniors. I believe the terms denial and enabling are appropriate to consider when relating to seniors. It is more convenient for us if the senior doesn't need our help. We visit and are in "denial" about their true state because the reality would require us to take some action. This action could be uncomfortable for us. We enable by encouraging them to be independent without ever questioning behavior that might be dangerous or harmful. We enable detrimental situations when we avoid contact in the name of independence. If we can think ahead of a need and then help with that need, our help is not as noticeable. It's back to the adage, "Don't take away their driver's license; take away their need to drive."

There are lots of community groups and activities for seniors. However, there is nothing better than family. Use these community services but recognize that many services deal with only one part of the situation and are not the whole solution. Our seniors still need us.

11.
Your Home, Not The Rest Home!

Keeping Them Home

There are some great life lessons we learn as we age. Most of us are very clear on how we would prefer to die. I'm like most of the people I know. My goal is to go from my home, not a rest home. My wife and I have a financial retirement plan. We have remodeled our house to make it more senior safe and old age friendly. We see our doctor regularly, eat right and take vitamins. She exercises. We are both mentally active and do other things to ensure that we have as good a quality of life as possible. We maintain an excellent relationship with our adult children and already seek their advice on certain issues. After all, our kids are more technologically oriented than we are.

Since I'm writing about and studying aging issues, it wouldn't be fair for me to not practice what I preach. I'm concerned with how the population ages. I see an entirely different model in the future. As the "Boomers" age, goods, services, the delivery of health care and the need for additional services change. One of the most important behaviors that must change is our willingness to accept help. The Boomer generation has changed virtually everything in our paths. Some changes were great and, in my opinion, some things need to be changed back.

I grew up believing in faith, family, friends, and work. I never thought about not getting up and going to work. I see reports today about how hard Americans work, how stressed we are at work and how little time off we get. Compared to what our parents faced coming off of the Depression and the hardships during World War II, we've got it pretty easy.

My Dad ran a service station and sold used cars. His typical work week was seven days. He took off a couple of hours each day and rode his horse.

There are many stories about the long hours and hard work of our parents' generation. Many in this older generation thought the ultimate sign of love for their family was to provide for them. They sacrificed time with family to ensure a meal on the table and a warm, safe place to live. Many people from this generation are not warm and fuzzy. They seem to be very committed to their husband or wife. The men grew up in the era when "men don't cry." They know what tough times are and generally are very self reliant. Our new generation can learn a lot about ethics, hard work, and family values from the previous generation.

The obvious missing trait in the older generation is not being good at accepting help. Our own generation has created the "welfare society." One of the older generation's sayings was, "I'd rather pick shit with the chickens than accept charity." The Boomers have created a society in which the largest portion of our federal budget is allocated to entitlement programs. Even thought these are by far the greatest federal and state expenditures they only assure care for a minority of people. In my opinion, many in this minority not only will accept assistance, they expect it.

The vast majority of U.S. citizens do not want, need, nor expect any government assistance. We are independent. Our parents were not conditioned to accept help and neither are we. If we don't want to end up in the rest home, we'd better learn how to accept some help.

In my business, I've noticed that the old folks are their own worst enemy. Perhaps this is true for all of us. We have older people for whom we care that have had care plans developed by their adult children. The old folks agree to the plan but, as soon as the children are gone, they change the plan and do what they want. They obviously are placating their children, then trying to re-establish their independence.

One client, Rose, came to us after a nursing home stay because of a fall. Rose has diminishing eyesight and tripped on an area rug. Since she is losing her eyesight, the Occupational Therapist, who did her home evaluation, removed the area rug. We were providing limited care three times per week. The care started at four hours per day, five days per week. As Rose recovered from the fall, she reduced her level of care. Mind you, Rose's eyesight is getting worse, not better. She is home alone and for safety reasons should be expanding her care. After three months, the area rug has reappeared and she has dropped her caregiver. You'd think she'd learn. The rug has already sent her to the nursing home once and it'll probably do it again. Even though she is feeling better, she isn't getting any younger and her eyesight is getting worse. But since she is feeling better physically, she doesn't want needed help. My wife reminds me that Rose has this "right."

My wife is a Licensed Clinical Social Worker and has a Masters Degree in Psychology. She explained to me that we have the right to self-determination. Even though our decisions may be detrimental to us, we still have the right to make them. I don't believe this right begins until we are seventeen and my wife believes at eighteen. If this woman was our dependent child, we could force her to live in a safe, secure place. With the adult right of self-determination, we can live wherever we can find a place. Think about the number of homeless. When the weather turns bad, we can invite them in but the law can't force them in. It is the same with old folks. You can move the rug and they can put it back. We are going to have to do a better job of educating the population about the new perils of aging.

Can You Keep Your Parents At Home?

There are some basic realities that are applicable to assisting our aging parents.

1. They must be willing to accept care!
2. They must be able to participate in their care!
3. They must be compliant with safety measures!
4. They must be committed to staying at home!
5. You must be committed to keeping them home!
6. The plan must be workable!
7. Someone must have the financial resources required!

Requirement One:

They must be willing to accept care! The companies providing home health care have an easier time with acceptance. The situation generally is that if someone wants to go home rather than to a nursing home, they must accept adequate help and care at home. When we considered bringing my Mom home, Dad had to agree to a twenty-four hour companion being with them. Of course, he would have agreed to anything to bring his bride of sixty-five years home. Once we got her home, it all changed.

They were both eighty-eight years old and Mom couldn't move without assistance. Dad was hard of hearing in one ear and deaf in the other. He couldn't hear Mom's call for help if needed. He also wasn't able to provide the personal hygiene care required. As with most husbands, he vastly overestimated his ability to deliver care. He said that he was all she had needed for sixty-five years. She was his sweetheart, and he would be the caregiver. Of course, he couldn't be. The introduction of a live-in companion is incredibly intrusive. Mom and Dad had never had anybody live in their country home with them. They had long since moved from the house where they raised their children. In their country home of twenty years, it had always just been them. This is not an easy situation for anyone. We try to make it the best we can. However, let's think ahead and ask, "How would we handle it?"

One of our first twenty-four hour "live-ins," Joan, was only adequately functional. I would guess she functioned at the level of someone about nine years old. She was a poor cook and had some very annoying habits. Dad really didn't like her. Mother, on the other hand, loved her. I think part of the attraction was how subservient she was. Joan helped Mom with her most personal needs and was very loyal to her. I sometimes thought Joan did some things intentionally just to irritate my father. During this time, I supplemented the food prepared because Joan couldn't cook. Mom liked her, and that was what I was trying to achieve. Things didn't have to be perfect, just acceptable. I repeat, "Things don't have to be perfect, just acceptable." Beware of being too particular. Perfection can undermine the purpose.

Billie, the companion sharing the duty, was an excellent cook and Dad loved her. Mom didn't like her as much and maybe was even a little jealous of her. Every other day I'd take Dad for a two hour ride. We just drove the country-side. Dad spent one and one-half hours of the ride venting about Joan, the caregiver he didn't like. One complaint was that she put their instant oatmeal in the microwave oven for ten minutes when the package clearly said one minute. Dad also complained about how much milk she poured for him. If he wanted a full glass, Joan poured a half. If he wanted half, she'd pour a full glass. Joan knew Mom would protect her, so I believe she did these things to irritate Dad. During the last thirty minutes of the ride, I'd explain to Dad that without a caregiver the family would move Mom back to the nursing facility. Of course he didn't want that to happen. I'd also ask him, "Do you want me to get someone else?" Dad said "no" because Mom really liked her and Joan provided good care for Mom. By the end of the ride, everything was all right; of course, I knew, only for a day. Begrudgingly, Dad allowed appropriate care until Mom passed away.

I believe the most common problem with aging is our inability to recognize and accept appropriate care. As our business Assisting Aging Parents moves forward, I become increasingly aware of this fact. It isn't the family trying to avoid costs or involvement that's been the biggest problem. It is the aging person's refusal to recognize and accept appropriate care. We've had contacts with the families of elderly people where the care needed is obvious; people starving, people who are fall risks, people needing to go to the doctor, and elderly who are incredibly fragile. We had a lovely once-a-week client who turned down our offer to take her to a needed doctor appointment because she thought she was better. She died within the week. We've had people who needed only a few hours of care per day who were ultimately put under another's guardianship because they refused simple care. They now are totally dependent although they haven't realized it yet. The cases go on and on. We talk with people at meetings and they describe how frustrating it is because their aging parents refuse vital care. We see them later and they report that a parent had an *avoidable* problem occur, which ultimately sent them to a nursing home; the last place they wanted to be. Most of them wouldn't have had to be there if they'd only listened. As we ourselves age, we better be smarter, and more receptive to accepting help. We generally become greater burdens in our attempt to not be burdens.

Requirement Two:

They must be able to participate in their care! Our aging parents must be able to participate in their care. They must not only verbally agree to accept help, but they need to be compliant with it. Sometimes a written contract can be helpful. When caring for both Mom and Dad, it was a continual battle to get Dad to give Mom her medications. We had their companion monitor this situation. Non-medical providers can prompt, remind, and observe, but they cannot dispense medications. Dad thought an anti-anxiety drug caused my mother to sleep excessively, so he wouldn't give it to her. After about three days of missing the medication, I would notice her crying or being unusually upset. At first, Dad swore the companion to secrecy and she complied. We took steps to correct this problem. We placed the medicine in a weekly dose pill case, which was identified by day of the week. One could easily see whether the medication was gone or not. We assured the companion that we must know whether or not the medication was administered and that she wouldn't get in any trouble for reporting. We threatened Dad with taking Mom back to the nursing home if he withheld her medication. Dad didn't believe in medicine and believed doctors would kill you. Our corrective step didn't fix the problem entirely although it improved. The most Mom missed under the new rules was one daily dose.

We know of a family, the Smiths, who prepare food for cousins who otherwise would go hungry. As long as the Smiths are there and eat with them, everything is fine. If food is left for upcoming meals, the cousins will not eat it. They get confused and are suspicious of where it came from even though it was left by a family member. The cousins no longer have the ability to nourish themselves so they require meal assistance.

The cousins, of course, won't allow any help; therefore, they don't have the ability to participate in their own care. In Dad's case, after mother died, we left a caregiver in place. Dad was ninety and needed no personal care although he had dementia. Burning logs would fall out of the fireplace or he lost or misplaced things he needed to survive. He also was not able to make adequate decisions about his nourishment or financial dealings. A funny thing occurred when the bank sent his order of new checks. There were at least four different pads. Dad wouldn't put the spares away, so he wrote checks from whichever pad he found at the time.

He never wrote any checks down, so balancing his check book was a "crap shoot."

Over time his dementia worsened. He became sexually aggressive toward his female caregivers. At first, the family didn't believe the accusations. After we read about and studied this issue, we learned that it is not uncommon. The caregivers all told the same story. When rebuked, he became very ugly. He cursed and belittled the caregivers and accused them of conspiring against him. I confronted him about this and he replied that they all got together and planned and plotted these false accusations to harm him. Of course, the various caregivers had no contact with one another at any time. He even accused one caregiver of stealing his ice cubes.

Dad was almost deaf. He was deaf in one ear and had about a 70% loss in the other. The use of a hearing aid did allow for some understanding. Dad continually refused to wear the hearing aid and consequently could not hear conversations or instructions. He stated that it was only essential for *him* to talk; he didn't "want to hear what anyone else had to say anyway!" His doctor prescribed some medication that would help his dementia and allow him to be a little more compliant. He refused to take any medications. He had a slight heart irregularity and would only take a baby aspirin. He had teeth that were infected and refused to have them pulled.

My sister then assumed the responsibility for managing his care and absolutely did the best she could under the circumstances. The family told Dad that there were three things he must do to stay home. He had only three simple things.

1. Keep your hands off the help and treat them with respect.
2. Wear your hearing aid.
3. Take your medications.

We would have accepted just keeping his hands off

the help as a last resort. Dad was 0 for 3. He couldn't or wouldn't be compliant on a regular basis. Ultimately my oldest brother was appointed guardian.

After many failed home care attempts, we put Dad in a dementia unit which forced some compliance. He hated the unit. All he had to do to go home was the three things listed above. He refused. While in the unit, the dementia worsened and he lost the ability to swallow. He was hospitalized to see if there was any way to effect a cure. He refused any type of tube or I.V. feeding, which meant he was terminal. We took him home to die. Before his admittance to the dementia unit, Dad proved his inability to participate in his own care.

You can have a dream of how you want to see them end their lives. You can do lots of things to make it possible. You can't make the starving eat. You couldn't make my Dad compliant, and you can't care for someone who won't let you. You can offer help, but you are ultimately powerless over their compliance. After all, they have the right to refuse help. They have the right to self-determination. If this occurs with your aging loved one, you'll have to recognize that you are powerless over this situation. Do the best you can but realize it's in God's hands, not yours.

Requirement Three:

They must be compliant with safety measures! This goes without saying. Sometimes it is a matter of them not being able to control their compliance. I've written about the Alzheimer's patient who was very fragile and a fall hazard. She got out of an unlocked door, fell on the step and broke her neck. There should have been door locks high enough that she couldn't reach them or she should have never been out of anyone's sight. Neither of these may have been practical. In lieu of these measures, she probably should have been institutionalized if possible. If she didn't know where she was or who she was, it was someone else's dream to keep her home, not hers.

I'm definitely a stay-at-home advocate but sometimes it just isn't possible. If your loved one is continually leaving pots and pans on a heated stove, it is a safety hazard. If they can't comply, they shouldn't stay. If they don't have the ability to call 911, you can provide some type of safety device they can wear. They must, however, wear it. This list can go on and on.

My point is, if they don't have the ability to understand and follow simple safety guidelines, they would be better off in a safe environment. In the first part of this book, I listed ten major safety areas of concern. Sit down with your aging parent and go over these items. Explain to them that this is not elective. They must be willing and able to comply. Of course, their rights may trump this. Remember, you have the right to detach. No matter how difficult this is, because of their attitude this may ultimately be the only option to save your sanity. When my wife Ann's mother was rapidly approaching disaster, this became a problem for her. She had some peace of mind knowing she had tried everything she knew to help. A professional got her mother to the right place for help. Many people will not seek help until their lives are a total disaster. Sometimes adult children, family, or friends are the last people who can help. It can take someone without an emotional history or investment to help ease the burden.

Requirement Four:
They must be committed to staying at home! My Mom and Dad were committed to dying in their own bed. The interesting thing about this is that it was all driven by my Dad. Mom knew that Dad couldn't or at least wouldn't function anywhere other than home. He couldn't hear and didn't like being around old people. My sister tried taking

him to a senior center for lunch and socialization. His comment was that there were too many old people there. He liked the outdoors, his dogs, cats, and garden. Any other place wasn't going to do.

My mother, on the other hand, said, "If Dad dies first, I'm moving to town to assisted living." Mom was more social and less mobile. She enjoyed talking with her children and caregivers and watching television. Some people are better off in retirement or assisted living or even in a nursing home.

This dying in your own bed takes a lot of commitment from everyone involved. I believe that the emphasis today is on placing the elderly in "rest homes," rather than allowing them to remain in their own homes. As an elder, you may have to convince your doctor, pastor, family and friends that you really are committed to staying home. You'll have to accept help, be compliant with instructions and participate to the best of your ability. You'll have to have enough financial resources that you are *willing* to spend. Some elders want to stay home but have no idea about current financial values. They haven't worked or hired anybody in years. They may not have made a major expenditure in years. Consequently, they have unrealistic expectations about what today's costs are. Our company, Assisting Aging Parents, is the least expensive service provider of our kind in the area, yet people still think it is too costly. Elders have worked hard for their money. They have managed to have resources to leave behind. A lot of them are so tight that they "squeak" when they walk. My question is, "If you aren't willing to spend it on yourself, why have it?"

My Dad wanted to leave us an estate. Each and every one of his children wanted him to spend it on him and Mom first. If nothing were left, we would have pitched in to keep them home. My kids would do the same for me. After all, we can't help you if you are not really committed to it.

Requirement Five:

✗ You must be committed to keeping them home!

This is a very difficult road. I believe it is worth it although many would disagree. Others shouldn't criticize your decision. Each situation is different. Do what is right for you and your family. If you do commit to helping your parents, you may be agreeing at some point to accept your parents as dependents. This can be much like the decision to have children. Your parents aren't going to get younger, better or need less help. They also may not be compliant voluntarily. You may need to change their care plan if circumstances change and you find it is more then you and your family are able to do. You should have end-of-life discussions and be willing, to the best of your ability, to honor their wishes.

I watched my parents go from being bright, proud, intelligent, fully self-sufficient and independent people to wearing Depends and being totally dependent. To see this, to handle this, to make it as good as it can be, requires commitment. The memories of your whole life, both good and bad, will surface. You will have to deal with these emotions continually. You will be required to set aside some of your emotions to concentrate on theirs. Once committed, it is not easy to turn back. Is it fair to your family? It is okay not to start. However, if you start and need to stop, you may have feelings of overwhelming guilt.

You may not be able to keep them home. If you elect to try, remember your best effort is all you have. Circumstances change as our parents age. We may not be in control of events. We may not be in control of health issues. Our lives change.

The elderly we interview would prefer dying in their home rather than a rest home. To facilitate this, you can try to make end-of-life decisions that are dignified and compassionate. Most of us are programmed to make life saving decisions, not life ending decisions. This is a huge responsibility. Part of your commitment is to adhere to the elder's end-of-life wishes, as opposed to your and the medical profession's life saving issues. You must consider whether they will have the quality of life they desire if you keep them alive artificially.

Granted, they may not make it easy for you to keep them at home. My Dad was physically healthy as a horse up until his last few months. He walked, cut wood and even chased the help. His dementia caused him to have a seven second delay from when he placed something in his mouth until he swallowed. This meant his body and brain couldn't work together to process his food or liquids. Without life saving interventions, it was only a matter of time before he would die. This was diagnosed while he was a patient at a local hospital. Besides dying, his other option was for I.V. or tube feeding either of which would have extended his life.

Dad hated hospitals, hated the dementia unit, didn't trust doctors and clearly would not take any required medications. He loved his home. He felt the presence of his wife (my mother) at home. He had his dogs and cats for comfort. His wish was to go home to die. He refused any artificial treatment that would have extended his life.

If you are committed, I encourage you to support and honor their decisions. Remember, you will have end-of-life-requests that you will want honored. Why would we encourage our parents to make different end-of-life decisions than we would make for ourselves? Hospices, in-home companions, and doctors are available to create as comfortable of an end-of-life situation as possible. Part of making your commitment is having conversations with your aging parents so you know their wishes.

Adult children are typically very uncomfortable with these discussions. They shouldn't be. Most aging parents know clearly what type of end-of-life experience they desire. They know and may not be uncomfortable discussing it. I had my Mother's doctor visit three different times and discuss her wishes. In the end, we didn't call the ambulance. The doctor prescribed morphine patches for comfort and to ensure no pain. We waited for her to pass and then phoned the funeral home. I must admit, in the last hours, I had to fight with myself to keep from calling an ambulance. In the end, I knew it was her desire I was honoring. I had made the commitment and I had to stand by that commitment. It was the right thing to do!

Requirement Six:

The plan must be workable! In a recent conversation with a family, I learned that their eighty year old mother, Violet, had a recent surgery on one of her ankles. Mom has plenty of money. Violet is very active in her church. When her church friends heard of her impending surgery, they offered to help. Church friends are a good source for food and some socialization. Many of these church members who offer help are old enough that lifting is out of the question. Also, Violet's family is involved in her care. Since the surgery was on an ankle, she has very limited mobility even with a walker and needs assistance moving around the house.

A daughter and her husband are the primary providers of care. They work day-shift jobs and are at work five days per week, creating an absence of eleven hours each day. They also frequently work overtime and have children in school. The void was to be filled by a friend, but there was some question about the friend's availability. Assistance was required for a minimum of two weeks and most likely for four weeks. The first couple of nights the family stayed with Mom. Since the children's school is closer to their residence and they have multiple pets, staying at Mom's wasn't practical.

Over the four week period, the friend ended up *not* filling the void. There were possible voids both through the day and overnight. The assumption was that Mom would be able to at least navigate to the bathroom. I'm sure she thought she could. I'm sure Mom wanted and liked the personal attention she was receiving. I'm also sure that when she was anticipating how much help she would need, she believed the church would be enough.

We know of a similar instance of an elderly female with an injury that caused her to be bedridden. She apparently had no family in the area and depended on help from her church, friends, and neighbors. She required so much attention that her friends began to avoid her in order to have any peace. She left the front door open with a note saying, "I'm upstairs, come on in."

Both of these women had the ability to pay for personal in-home care, but would not. In one case, the person became a "burden" on relatives. In the other, she became a burden on her friends. As we age, we need to retain some judgment about our proper care. It is okay to use family and friends when they are able to help. There may come a time when this is our only option. Let's save this option until it is needed most. Let us consider what we are asking them to do. Are we burdening them when we can pay for services that can help?

Requirement Seven:

Someone must have the financial resources required! There are multiple resource options depending on your resources and what you have planned. For low income seniors in Missouri, Medicaid will provide some in-home services, not all of which must be medically necessary. Some people qualify for veterans' benefits. Some have long-term care insurance. Medicare and most insurance policies will only pay for medically necessary services. The most required service that enables people to stay in their homes is assistance with daily living activities. Most long-term care policies, Medicaid policies and even veterans' policies require a certification of need. Medical professionals or Social Workers are required to evaluate the situation and create a care plan that satisfies the requirements of the insurer.

In Greene County Missouri, 92.5% of the population sixty-five or over is not classified as low income. The average household income for this group is $39,821. 78.5% are living in owner occupied housing. What this tells us is that 92.5% of our local population is going to have to pay for their own services. If admitted to a nursing home, they will have to pay for their own care until their assets reduce to the level required to meet Medicaid guidelines.

Another stipulation is that elders must be willing to *use* their resources to pay for their care. Most studies show there is wealth accumulated by our elder society. Elders (sixty-two and over) who own their own homes can reverse mortgage the home in order to have access to equity to pay for their care. Our business is structured for those who are self-pay. I'm trying to develop the delivery of services to seniors who otherwise don't have access. Those with low income are the focus of all the social service and welfare programs. What about the people with their own money? A lot of seniors have set aside money for their later years. Also, a lot of today's seniors have come through the Depression and World War II. They may not have a good understanding of the cost of care in today's dollars. Another issue is the willingness to pay, both on the part of the elderly and their families.

An example of possible resources could be: A couple buys one-hundred acres in 1934 and starts a family farm. They produce food, milk and garden items for them to eat. They also produce cattle, milk, hay, etc. for sale. Most of the items they purchase probably can be expensed to the farm so it is likely they show very little profit, if any, over the years. Social Security is based on earnings and if you are a farmer you probably are self-employed. You pay Social Security as a self employment tax based on your reported earnings. If, over the years, you reported little or no earnings, your Social Security account doesn't grow. At retirement you would qualify for minimal Social Security. When unable to continue farming, you would have to live on your savings plus the minimal Social Security payments. You want to pass the family farm to your children. After all, you spent your life building it to what it is today. You cherish the farm and its memories.

This is the place Peter was born and then along came Paul and Mary. With expansions, your home is 3,000 square feet and modernized with improvements over time. How could you give this up? Your home place, after all these years, has changed in fair market value. In my area, unimproved land is now worth $12,000 per acre. Improved with a barn and outbuilding, the value now would be at least $1.6 million.

I hear family farmers saying, "I've worked all my life and never made any money." The lowest evaluation in our area for this property would value this investment at $600,000. I believe that starting with nothing and then having an asset of $600,000 to $1.6 million is making money! At sixty-two years of age, you can qualify for a reverse mortgage which can give you adequate cash to care for you until you depart this earth. Families should consider all resources and be willing to apply them where they help the most.

12.
Allowing The Care Plan To Work: Letting Go Of control

As I observe our journey, it is filled with transition. Each of us in the journey is in transition. There is a beginning and an end and we all are somewhere in the journey. Our children are not as far along as we are. Our elders are ahead of us. We are all moving in the same direction. This is very simple to write about but there is nothing simple about it. If we have been the primary caregivers for our parents and finally recognize that there must be more help, accepting the help is a transition.

The older I get, the more complex life appears. There are more forces at work, more people in play, more health challenges, and my financial situation changes. The older I get, the simpler I must make my life. Remember the beginning. The breast or bottle, poop, cry, and sleep. At the end, the breasts are a memory (this is purely a male thing: I could have said they're just hanging around now) and we've probably been off the bottle for years. We still poop, cry, and sleep. The journey begins simply, then steadily crescendos to complexity.

Our responsibility is to manage the transition. We must be able to focus, keep our eye on the ball and know our ultimate goal. My company has a couple of cases that best illustrate my point. In both cases, the families are committed to keeping the elders at home until their deaths, if at all possible. In both cases, the family has been providing the necessary supplemental care required to keep these people home. Over time the workload and care required has increased. It has been increasing on a continual basis and now additional help is required. The family caregivers have scraped, clawed, finagled, manipulated, cooked, cleaned, driven and every other thing possible to help. The caregivers are worn out! Their goal is still there but there just aren't enough of them to go around. The required care becomes more constant.

We all build habits and patterns. It is essential to how we function. We also embed our identities with our habits, functions, patterns, and goals. We identify with our mission and, in a sense, become it. If we provide care for a loved one twenty hours per week, this becomes part of our pattern, routine, habit, and who we are. We may not be able to do more but are deeply connected with our current level of activity. These actions can become a "control thing" for us and we balance ourselves with these activities.

When we put outside care in place, it upsets our balance. We are afraid of losing control. The quick answer is to put in place new control points and enjoy the new help but that's too easy. It seems simple to an outsider. Our elders don't manage change very well and neither do we. In both of these cases, food is an issue. The family caregivers have already developed their own way of feeding and providing food for their elder. When you add an outside caregiver, if you're not careful, you've just added another mouth to feed.

One of our client's would buy, bring to the house, and prepare the evening meal. She wasn't able to do this every night so would sometimes leave leftovers. She was intent on preparing quality, gourmet meals from scratch for her elders to enjoy. She was working herself silly. She confided in me that the elders really loved hamburgers. They also had a passion for cookies and beer. These don't sound like gourmet eaters to me. The caregiver wanted them to be. We placed a fulltime caregiver into the house. What I noticed next was there was one more mouth for the family caregiver to feed causing her more work and more responsibility. Accepting outside help is a major transition for a caregiver. This is one example of a family member's need to relinquish some control in order for the situation to work best for her loved ones.

The family caregiver needs to relinquish her former role as caregiver and take on her new role as overseer. (This is actually less work and more enjoyable.) The obvious answer to an outsider is for the family member to shop and deliver adequate food for the household. Then, allow the hired caregiver to prepare the meals. The household will move from a schedule based on the family member to an independent schedule. The family member who formerly was the caregiver could now actually visit and eat meals prepared by the hired caregiver.

Instead of welcoming help, we have a problem with giving up control and the activity and, perhaps, even part of our identity. Think of the time we've spent. What will we do with ourselves? It might seem odd to an outsider but we know who we were, what we were doing, why we were doing it, and when and where we were supposed to be. Our life was in order. It may have seemed chaotic to outsiders but, to us, it was in order. For the ultimate good of our elderly loved one, we need to change. We no longer are able to provide adequate care. We must relinquish control, turn over the reins to an outsider. We must yield, heaven forbid, we must reschedule. The funny thing is, we will be far better off and so will our elder. Accept the change, embrace the transition and look forward to restoring a family relationship with your elder. You no longer must provide care. Now you can provide love, support and, more importantly, understanding. With the proper help, you can try to make their wishes come true. It is, however, too big of a burden to carry by yourself.

In another case, the family actually cooked and delivered the food. If they weren't going to deliver for a particular meal, they ensured there was food on site. Their intentions, however, were to cook every meal, deliver it and share it. Consequently, there was no food in the house except the occasional leftover. If the elder wanted a hot dog, the family would get one or two from their package and deliver it. (The houses were nearby) They would split orange juice, milk and any other perishable foods. When our full-time caregiver arrived, the dynamics changed. Now there was another mouth to feed; more likes and dislikes, more work, and more responsibility for the family. I strongly advise families to either accept a grocery list from the caregiver or allow the caregiver to do the shopping. In either case, let the caregiver prepare the meals. If you choose to prepare the meals be *absolutely certain* that there will be ample food when you are unavailable. Think about what you would like to eat. If you don't want a peanut butter sandwich for lunch every day, then they probably don't either.

Part of this cycle is to micro-manage. We place control for the sake of control. We do it because we can do it. It is power! It also creates an enormous amount of activity. It gives us something to do. It fills our voids. We wouldn't do all of this if it didn't satisfy something within us. We think we are doing it for the greater good, a higher calling, to facilitate the dream and to ensure that the elder lives at home. This very mission becomes our identity, who we are, what we stand for. What we've really done is to make everything totally dependent on us, our schedule, in our time frame, on our agenda. This may not work for a separate household.

The problem with this setup is that if something happens to us, grandma may not get fed. What happens when we get sick or have a stress induced heart attack? Recognize that stress is a killer. If something happens to us, grandma may not get medical care or her essential needs met. If we truly want grandma to stay home until the end, we will *al-*

low the care to work. We'll put in adequate care. We'll stock the refrigerator and cupboards. We'll insure there are adequate supplies. We'll oversee the help, not deliver the care. We will release the artificial controls and stop micro-managing. We will allow the elder's household to go on its own schedule. We'll become family again. We'll visit, we'll love, we'll support, we'll understand, and we'll be there for them in the end. We won't be so burned out and sick that we won't be able to truly be there when they need us the most.

There seems to be one common thread running through all of our cases. It is food! It is control of quantity, quality, substance and every other item connected with food. It must be our last chance to impose some of our will on our parents. Maybe it is getting even with how they raised us? You know, "Eat your spinach, vegetables, clean your plate, and don't eat sweets." Do you remember all the di-etary rules? Virtually all of our caregivers complain about the family's lack of supply or willingness to allow Mom or Grandpa to eat what they want. Ask yourself, "What am I saving them from?" We should assure that our elders are getting their essential nourishment, then loosen up a little. At ninety, what is it going to hurt if they eat a hot dog or have beer and cookies? It seems that, as our lives diminish, the last thing we can enjoy is our food. We have trouble walking, hearing, talking, seeing, breathing, sleeping, pee-ing, pooping, and driving. Why can't we, at least, get a good last meal? Why do families get hung up on incredibly strict diets? Why do we cause all this grief when it could be so easy? We think we are doing the right thing. But can it be a control thing? Get over it. Let them decide what they like as long as basic nutritional needs are met. Why don't we make this as easy as we can for us and as pleasant as we can for our elderly!

One big question facing families who add adequate outside care is, "What do I do with my new-found time?" Take up a hobby, travel, fish, shop, read, go to movies or anything else; just enjoy having your life back.

My company gives people their lives back. I'm not talking about just the family caregiver; I'm talking about the elderly as well. If you put the appropriate care in place, the elder has his or her own schedule and life, and so do you. Your daily life will not be without contact or involvement with your elder, but you will devote the appropriate amounts of commitment and resources and time. You can actually have a quality of life and so can your elder. Nobody wants to be a burden. This point may be the most important I'll give you. I write in this book about the elder accepting care. The elder must be able to allow and accept the appropriate care for their wishes to be fulfilled. You must be able to allow this care to take place. Nobody goes it alone. This is not the time to "die on your own sword." Manage the transitions, accept the care, allow the care, and help everyone arrive at the end with dignity.

13.
Whose Life Is It?

I strongly believe in using available resources to allow people to have a quality, not quantity, end-of-life. Another point! Remember, when working with the elderly, it's their life and their wishes! The elderly fear that, if they need some help, the kids will come in with "guns blazing" and take over their lives. Due to this fear, many elderly will cover up or hide deficiencies to keep us from detecting weaknesses. We treasure our independence and our kids will damn well treasure theirs when it's their turn!

As we move into the roles of caregivers, it is of the utmost importance to allow the elderly to retain their dignity as well as their independence. In some form, they still need to feel they are in control of their lives; that they still have a say in their treatment, living conditions, and care plans. After all, it is their end-of-life issues, not ours.

This can be difficult to understand because their ends-of-life issues certainly do impact us. This can bring up years of unfinished emotional business. We don't want them to leave us or there may be no time left for them to be the sort of parent we had hoped they would someday become. There may never be the relationship we had hoped for. They may even no longer be capable of hearing the things we've never said and may still need to say. We must lay all these issues aside and consider what our parents want at the end of their lives. This is the "right" thing to do. When it is our turn, we will want to make our own end-of-life decisions and have them honored.

Alice is a female acquaintance who has a daughter named Kathy. They both have very definite ideas about clothing styles that are directly opposite from each other. They love each other very much but never agree on color or style of clothing. Kathy continually tries to get her mother to dress differently. Alice has dressed herself for years and wears comfortable, pleasant clothing that makes her feel good. Kathy wants her mother to dress in a more youthful style. Alice often says that the worst imaginable thing that could happen to her would be to become incapacitated and have Kathy dress her as she chooses. This may be a silly point. However, it is the point that it is our life, our likes, and our view of style, not our children's. This is not a time to get back or gain some form of control over our parents. As we were growing up, many of us were trying to get out from under the control of our parents and become our "own person." Later, we want to become independent and productive citizens of society.

As children mature, many parents relinquish control and develop independent adult relationships with their children; some good, some bad, but independent nonetheless. The last thing a parent wants is to become dependent on their children. This is partly because the parent doesn't want to be a burden on the children nor cause them to expend time or money they could spend on their current families. Also, the parent doesn't want to give up his or her lifestyle, independence, and ability to be in control of his life. This is a huge factor in the aging process. Who is in control?

The life cycle is simple: We start out crying and pooping our pants and, if we live long enough, we go out crying and pooping our pants. Life is what we do to fill up the time in-between. We start by doing everything possible to become independent and we end by clinging to that independence. The biggest mission we can undertake as adult children is to be able to help and care for our aging parents as softly and gently as we can. We need to help without them

94

noticing. Think ahead of their needs and anticipate the things they might try to do that will place them in harm's way. The best way is to provide both the physical and emotional support needed to help our aging parents live and complete their lives as they wish. Don't take over the end of their lives. They've lived long and hard and deserve the right to end according to their own terms.

14.
Caring For The Caregiver

After personally experiencing firsthand what it is to be the caregiver, I created Assisting Aging Parents. The purpose is to help with the pressures faced when caring for your parent or aging loved one. We now have the Sandwich Generation, who are caring for children and parents at the same time. The need for elder care is growing and expanding. Because of aging of the baby boom generation, the numbers are mind boggling! Elders and adult children simply aren't prepared for what lies ahead. The streaks of independence in both groups can clash. Our journeys of being raised by our parents (with all the baggage that can entail) and then becoming responsible for them are seldom easy.

The following ideas are for anyone helping the caregiver, the caregiver or for anyone providing respite. The burnout for caregivers is a real issue. The longer someone lives, the more difficult it is to care for them. We spend enormous amounts of time helping them as they age. Then, when they need us the most, we wear out or burn out. We need some relief and need other family members to support us. If there are multiple siblings, consensus can be very difficult if not impossible to reach. The caregiver is the closest person to the aging parent and is the easiest to "guilt."

I've also seen a circumstance wherein a long-term caregiver named "Constance" worked on specific therapeutic techniques with a parent. Over time it began to pay dividends. In advance of a visit by an out-of-town sibling named Clarence, a local non attentive sibling called "Flash" engaged in a few meaningless activities with the parent. When Clarence arrived, "Flash", the generally non-attentive sibling said, "See what I've done with Mom and how much progress she's making." Clarence lavished a great deal of praise when it was least deserved. Constance, the devoted long-term caregiver, was the one who impacted the change. Flash's actions were for show. Imagine how Constance felt. Knowing this caregiver, I'm sure that the positive results with the parent were satisfaction enough; yet it would have been more rejuvenating if she had received some positive recognition for her good work. Caregivers for the elderly are very special people. Many put their lives on hold for an aging parent.

Another pitfall that long-term caregivers may have is the level of involvement with the aging person. They experience the struggle for life with the person every day. They become emotionally attached to this struggle and are driven by creating the best quality of life possible at the end-of-life. When the end is near, sometimes they confuse their own feelings with the wishes of the person for whom they care. There was a circumstance in which the elder's wishes were to die at home in her own bed without any life-saving measures. When the elderly person, Ruth, started to fail, her caregiver, Nancy, wanted measures taken to extend her life including hospitalization. Nancy was so caught up in delivering care that it had become "who she was." Part of her internal agenda was extending Ruth's life so she could continue her care. The delivery of care was an activity which she would have to replace. The end of Ruth's life would also cause incredible grieving and loss.

Generally speaking, I believe grieving is "us feeling empty and sorry for ourselves." If we believe that there are worse things that can happen to us than death or if Christians believe in life everlasting or if we believe people should be able to die with dignity, then when someone dies, isn't it a victory? When you are grieving, a good question to ask is, "If I could wish the person back to life, would they be happy?" When it comes to the senseless loss of life, I have a whole different outlook. When death comes at the end of a natural life or at the end of a long, hard health struggle, it can be a mercy and a victory. Providing supportive care to the caregiver plus understanding what she or he is going through is of the utmost importance. Be glad there are caring and compassionate caregivers in this world.

I have downloaded the following information about caring for the caregiver.

Aging Parents and Adult Children Together (A/PACT)

CARING FOR THE CAREGIVER

(Ninth in a 10-part series)

Marcy is divorced with two teenage sons. Her 81-year-old widowed father lives nearby. Over the past two years, Marcy's father has experienced major bouts of forgetfulness and depression, with increasing frailty due to arthritis and congestive heart failure. He has fallen several times during dizzy spells and sometimes forgets to take his arthritis and heart medications.

Marcy's job requires her to work significant overtime. While she needs the extra money, she recently had to refuse work because her father needed her at her home, where he was recuperating after a fall. During his three-week stay, Marcy realized how difficult it would be to have her father and sons living with her in her small, two-bedroom house.

Her father is back in his own home now, but Marcy feels guilty and is concerned about leaving him alone. She calls several times a day and stops in to check on him before and after work. Now the calls and visits are creating problems at work and at home with her sons. Marcy is exhausted from trying to balance everyone's needs, and feels alone.

While Marcy is a fictional character, growing numbers of adult children can relate to the situation described here. Perhaps you are caring for one of the 7.3 million older people – parents, relatives and friends — in this country who now need help with their daily activities.

A few statistics set the scene. Life expectancy at birth in the United States rose to 76.1 years in 1996, passing the record of 75.8 years in 1992. According to the U.S. Department of Labor, the "oldest old" — those aged 85 and older — were one of the fastest growing age groups between 1990 and 1995. The numbers help explain why a 1997 survey by the National Alliance for Caregiving and the American Association of Retired Persons found that in some 22.4 million homes in the United States — nearly a quarter of U.S. households — someone was caring for an older relative or friend. What are these caregivers doing? Typically, they spend 18 hours a week taking the person they care for to doctors, managing the elder's finances, helping with grocery shopping and providing hands-on personal care. Two-thirds of the caretakers also are employed. Of these, slightly more than half have had to make workplace accommodations — such as coming in late, leaving early, dropping back to part-time work or even passing up promotions — to provide eldercare.

Previous articles in the A/PACT series addressed issues surrounding the needs of older people. What about you — the caregiver — stretched by the conflicting demands of jobs, families and caregiving? How can you find — and keep — that crucial balance that lets you help others without neglecting yourself? It's not easy, but help is available and the range and variety of support is growing.

If you work for a large company, chances are that your employer can be a good resource. Many corporations now are training line supervisors, human resources staff and employee assistance professionals to help employees find the resources they need to cope with caregiving. Small and mid-sized companies may not yet have eldercare programs in place. If your company does not provide services, consider talking with the personnel department about your needs.

Services that companies can provide to help their caregiver employees include flextime and telecommuting options, lunchtime seminars, counseling, support groups and information and referral services. In addition, under the Family and Medical Leave Act, companies with more than 50 employees must grant employees unpaid leave to care for a sick family member.

For More Information

Working or not, caregivers can take advantage of the vast array of information available for caregivers and care recipients, including *caregiver newsletters* such as the *Caregiving Newsletter, Caring* and *Today's Caregiver.*

Supportive groups include the National Family Caregivers Association and Children of Aging Parents. Some organizations have local chapters with support groups; others are available through hospitals, adult day-care centers and area agencies on aging.

Books and videos include: *How to Care for Your Aging Parents* by Virginia Morris, *Baby Boomer's Guide to Caring for Aging Parents* by Bart Astor, and *Survival Tips for New Caregivers*, a video available from the American Association of Retired Persons (AARP) at P.O. Box 51040, Washington, DC 20091. Enclose a check for $4.00, payable to AARP.

On the *Internet*, visit the Family Caregiver Alliance *(www. caregiver.org)* and the caregiving chat room sponsored by AARP *(www.aarp.org)*. These sites offer tips and an opportunity to share experiences.

You also can contact the following organizations for additional information:

National Family Caregivers Association
10605 Concord Street, Suite 501
Kensington, MD 20895-2505
(301) 942-6430; (800) 896 3650; fax: (301) 942-2302
www.nfcacares.org

Children of Aging Parents
Woodbourne Office Campus
Suite 302-A
1609 Woodbourne Road
Levittown, PA 19057
(215) 945-6900

National Alliance for Caregiving
Montgomery Building
4720 Montgomery Lane
Bethesda, MD 20814-5320
(301) 718-8444

Well Spouse Foundation
P.O. Box 801
New York, NY 10023
(212) 644-1241
The Foundation provides referrals to support group of partners of the chronically ill.

Family Caregiver Alliance
425 Bush Street, Suite 500
San Francisco, CA 94108
(415) 434-3388
www.caregiver.org
The Alliance provides resources primarily for California residents.

Alzheimer's Association National Headquarters
919 North Michigan Avenue, Suite 1000
Chicago, IL 60611-1676
(800) 272-3900
www.alz.org

Eldercare Locator Service
(800) 677-1116
www.ageinfo.org/elderloc

Prepared by the National Alliance for Caregiving and the National Family Caregivers Association

To order the complete A/PACT series, contact: Consumer Response Center, Federal Trade Commission, Washington, DC 20580, 202-FTC-HELP (382-4357), TDD: 1-866-653-4261.

15.
What To Do If You Live Far Away Or Are Too Overwhelmed To Help?

What do you do if you live too far away or are too overwhelmed to help? If there is another family member nearby who is helping, you can help financially or give the caregiver a break by providing respite when you can. But what if there is no other family member living nearby? One possible answer is hire a Geriatric Care Manager. The following reference material from A/PACT addresses this subject.

Aging Parents and Adult Children Together (A/PACT)

SELECTING A GERIATRIC CARE MANAGER

(Eighth in a 10-part series)

Your elderly aunt is widowed and lives alone. You're the only family member she has to care for her. Her long-time health problems have become debilitating. You know she needs help but, because you live far away, you don't know exactly what she needs or where to look for help. Someone suggests that you contact a geriatric care manager. What is a care manager and how can you find a good one?

A geriatric care manager (GCM) is a professional who specializes in helping older people and their families with long-term care arrangements. GCMs often have training in gerontology, social work, nursing or counseling. They also have extensive knowledge about the cost, quality and availability of services in an older person's community. As a result, GCMs can help:

- Conduct care-planning assessments to identify problems and determine eligibility for assistance and the need for services;
- Screen, arrange and monitor in-home help or other services;
- Review financial, legal or medical issues and offer referrals to geriatric specialists to avoid future problems and conserve assets;
- Provide crisis intervention;
- Act as a liaison to families living away from the parent, making sure things are going well and alerting families to problems;
- Help move an older person to or from a retirement complex, care home or nursing home;
- Provide consumer education and advocacy; and,
- Offer counseling and support.

Choose a GCM carefully. The field of geriatric care management is relatively unregulated and many people without specialized training identify themselves as care managers, care coordinators or care advisors. Therefore, it's wise to screen candidates to ensure that you're working with a person qualified in this new profession.

Ask about candidates' training, education and background in care management and geriatrics. Ask how long they've been a GCM and whether they belong to the National Association of Professional Geriatric Care Managers or any other professional associations.

A care manager's ability to be responsive is important. Ask candidates what their average response time is to return calls from clients and their families. Have them describe their communication system: Do they use pagers, portable phones, an answering service or voice mail? Learn about their agency's size, hours and staff composition. How are after-hours emergencies handled? What are the back-up systems for covering vacations and days off? Will you and your parent work with one GCM or several?

Determine the scope of the GCM's practice. Some GCMs or agencies specialize in assessments and care consultation but typically don't follow people on an ongoing basis. An assessment is a thorough review of the client's physical, medical and mental status, and financial resources. It serves as the basis for a comprehensive plan for the client. Other GCMs offer psychotherapy, money management, or home care. They also can act as conservators, appointed by a court to manage the financial and/or personal affairs of someone unable to manage his or her own affairs. It's important that the GCM's practice setting and specialties meet your needs and your parent's.

Investigate the GCM's track record and reputation. Ask for letters of reference or names of previous clients you may contact. Is the GCM active in professional associations? Does the GCM perform volunteer work?

While there are no licensing requirements for GCMs, there are certification programs. Ask each candidate you interview if he or she is certified, and by whom.

Confusion about fees and billing can be a problem. Be sure you understand the GCM's billing rates and how charges are calculated. Fees vary depending on the GCM's work setting — private practice, public agency or private non-profit agency. Get a written service agreement that outlines the fee structure and practices.

Finally, ask GCM candidates if they subscribe to a code of ethics or are guided by professional standards of practice. Get a copy of the standards. They should deal with the right to privacy, fiduciary responsibilities, full disclosure, fostering self-determination, fees, continuing education and professional relationships. Ask how complaints are handled.

For More Information
You can find GCMs through:

• The Area Agency on Aging in your parent's community
• Hospitals, senior centers, geriatric assessment centers and charitable organizations, such as the Alzheimer's Association
• The National Association of Professional Geriatric Care Managers at (520) 881-8008
• The Eldercare Locator Service at (800) 677-1116

Private non-profit organizations that promote standards for geriatric care managers include:

National Association of Professional Geriatric Care Managers
1604 North Country Club Road
Tucson, AZ 85716-3102
(520) 881-8008; Fax: (520) 325-7925

National Council on Aging
409 Third Street, SW
Suite 200
Washington, DC 20024
(202) 479-1200; fax: (202) 479-0735

Case Management Society of America
8201 Cantrell Road, Suite 230
Little Rock, AR 72227
(501) 225-2229; fax: (501) 221-9068

Prepared by the National Association of Professional
Geriatric Care Managers

Eric's Comments

Of course I think the Geriatric Care Manager is a wonderful idea. This was the first person we added to our staff. I'm in this field because of passion and the fact that I've faced and handled the situations I write about with my parents or friends. Since 1997, I've been trying to understand the aging process and improve the quality of life as we age. My first Care Manager was a Licensed Clinical Social Worker with many years of experience who joined the National Association of Geriatric Care Managers. She continually updated her skills on Alzheimer's, legal, financial, safety and other senior issues. Her code of ethics placed the care and welfare of her client above all else. When she left to return to child welfare work, a Licensed Nursing Home Administrator replaced her. Since she has personally delivered care, she brings a fresh insight into our business. She also is well aware of the importance of keeping elders in their own home as long as possible and the attributes required in good caregivers.

In my opinion, when choosing a Geriatric Care Manager, you should avoid those who are affiliated with Health Care providers. Whose interests should be best served? I believe the best interests of the elderly should be served in the most economical manner. My concern with those affiliated with health care is; they do a good job of representing the interests of health care. However, I don't think they see the same picture that a non-medical senior advocate sees. The focuses are different. Locally, there is a Geriatric

Care Manager who owns a home health agency. They do a good job of providing medical services. The charge for their personal non-medical services is approximately 30% higher than mine. Before I opened Assisting Aging Parents, they used supplemental staffing from my agency. Now they view me as a competitor and no longer use my caregivers as supplemental staff.

I point this out for two reasons. First, we are using the same employee or candidate base, same qualifications, same or similar pay, so it isn't a matter of employee quality. Second, if the needs of the elderly could be provided at a 30% cost reduction, wouldn't that be in the best interest of the elderly? The same is true for all other health care providers in our area. They don't refer to us when they can use their own people even though their charges are higher than ours. So I ask, "Why pay more?" Be sure that the best interests of your elderly loved ones are paramount for any caregiver you consider.

16.
Assisted Living Facilities/Retirement Homes

The following is downloaded from the A/Pact website.

Aging Parents and Adult Children Together (A/PACT)

ALTERNATIVE LIVING ARRANGEMENTS

(Fourth in a 10-part series)

Your mother is 78 years old and lives alone. Her eyesight is failing, she's becoming forgetful and she's finding it difficult to keep up with housekeeping, home repairs and maintenance. You fear that she can't manage on her own much longer.

Many older people find it necessary or sometimes just more convenient to move to housing where housekeeping, recreational and other services are available. Fortunately, housing options abound. Among the choices these days are *independent living facilities, continuing care retirement communities, supportive housing* and *congregate care*. Some facilities are privately owned; others are government supported or sponsored by religious or other non-profit groups. The distinctions among facilities aren't always clear cut: The way a facility describes itself may provide little or no indication of the services it offers.

Here are some general guides to help you explore housing options with someone you love. *Independent living facilities* offer recreational and social programs, but few services. However, an independent living facility might be found within a *continuing care retirement community (CCRC)*, where housing options vary by need. A CCRC lets seniors enter while they're still active and independent, knowing that if they become infirm, services are available to meet their changing needs.

Housing options that fall between independent living facilities and nursing homes include *supportive housing, congregate care, board and care, personal care* and *assisted living facilities*. All provide housing and varying levels of health or supportive services. For example, assisted living may refer to a single-family home that provides shelter and care to a small group of residents or a large complex that houses hundreds of people.

What programs are called, and the care and services they provide, vary by state — sometimes even within a state. Some facilities offer at least one meal a day and light housekeeping; others include transportation to shopping and medical appointments. Some have staff that administer medication and coordinate residents' health care; in others, staff provides skilled nursing care. Add *federally subsidized apartments* to the mix. While these facilities for low-income seniors don't provide services, they may have a service *coordinator* to help residents get services.

The federal government regulates nursing homes and federally subsidized housing. By contrast, state governments are responsible for regulating and licensing assisted living and other housing programs for older people, but the laws that apply and the agencies that are responsible vary by state. However, every state has a long-term care ombudsman program to investigate issues involving nursing homes, board and care homes and other long-term care facilities. Some long-term care ombudsman programs also help residents of assisted living facilities.

The state or local area agency on aging can help you explore housing options. Many agencies distribute directories or guides to housing options for older people and people with disabilities in their service areas. Area agencies on aging also can direct you to the long-term care ombudsman program, which in turn can supply information about a particular facility. In addition, your parents may have friends and relatives living in senior housing facilities who can provide suggestions and recommendations.

When you consider alternative housing arrangements, think about the older person's needs and preferences. Start with the basics:

- What living conditions does a housing program offer?
- What services are provided?
- How much will it cost?
- Will the program meet this person's current health and safety needs and those you may anticipate?
- Who will decide the services the person receives?
- How much independence will he or she have?
- What are the older person's legal rights if he or she disagrees with the facility?

Before deciding on a facility, visit the premises and talk with staff, residents, and family members — theirs and yours. Before you sign a contract, read it carefully and ask a lawyer to review it.

For More Information

American Association of Retired Persons
Fulfillment
601 E Street, NW
Washington, DC 20049
www.aarp.org/caregive/cgsgaarp.htm
AARP offers several free pamphlets about housing options for older adults. Particularly helpful is *Home Away From Home: A Consumer Guide to Board and Care Homes* and *Assisted Living*, Stock No. D12446. Refer to the stock number when ordering.

American Association of Homes and Services for the Aging
900 E Street, NW, Suite 500
Washington, DC 20004-2937
(800) 675-9253 or (202) 783-2242
www.aahsa.org
This provider organization offers consumer information about continuing care retirement communities and assisted living on its Web site and publishes *Consumer's Directory of Continuing Care Retirement Communities*, which is available for $33.50, including shipping and handling.

Assisted Living Federation of America
10300 Eaton Place, Suite 400
Fairfax, VA 2030
(703) 691-8100
www.alfa.org
This provider organization offers consumer information about assisted living on its website.

Consumer Coalition on Assisted Living
2342 Oak Street
Falls Church, VA 22046
(703) 228-5243
This grassroots membership organization was founded in 1995 by consumers, providers, advocates, researchers and others to explore critical issues in assisted living.

Institute for Health Policy
Heller School, Brandeis University
415 South Street
Waltham, MA 02254
(800) 456-9966
www.brandeis.edu/heller/ihp.html
This university affiliated research institute on assisted living publishes a consumer guide, *Finding the Assisted Living Program for You*. It also offers additional information and discussion groups on its website.

American Bar Association Commission on Legal Problems of the Elderly
740 15th Street, NW
Washington, DC 20005-1022
(202) 662-8690; fax: (202) 662-8698
www.abanet.org/elderly
The Commission publishes the *ABA Legal Guide for Older Americans*, containing information about consumer legal issues, including housing options. The cost is $13.00.

For the state or local area on aging, check the government listings in the telephone book or contact the Eldercare Locator (800) 677-1116; *www.ageingo.org/elderloc*.

Prepared by The American Bar Association Commission on Legal Problems of the Elderly

Eric's Comments

Although I believe that people do better in their own homes, some people may do better in retirement living homes or communities. There are many people in retirement living situations and, in my opinion, this is also a "home setting," not a nursing or care facility. The obvious advantages with alternative living arrangements are social contact with peers and the support of groups of peers who also face aging and dying issues. My wife's mother lived in an excellent assisted living facility which offered many activities. She made many friends. This offered her the opportunity to function at her highest ability.

17.
Choosing A Safe Nursing Home

I downloaded the following from the Missouri Department of Health and Senior Services. They have some very good information and their link is www.dhss.mo.gov, then look for the senior services icon.

I think the bottom line is, how would you want to be considered and treated if these decisions where for you? While alternative living really would mean anything outside of their home of many years, I've focused more on nursing home living. Remember, the key word here is "living." There are many nice retirement living, assisted living, or retirement communities that become home to the elderly. Generally, the seniors will be able to make these decisions. They may need more help with the nursing home decision. Since this is such a huge issue, I have provided multiple downloads.

Do all facilities provide the same services and care ?

No, there are four levels of care provided by these facilities:

- A Residential Care Facility I (RCFI) provides shelter, board and protective oversight; this may mean it keeps and distributes medications and provides care during short-term illnesses or recuperation.
- A Residential Care Facility II (RCFII) provides additional services, including supervision of diets and assistance with An Intermediate Care Facility (ICF) provides board, personal care, basic health and nursing

117

care services under the direction of a licensed physician and daily supervision of a licensed nurse.

- A Skilled Nursing Facility (SNF) provides board, skilled nursing care and treatment services commonly performed by or under the supervision of a registered professional nurse. Individuals living in an SNF require twenty-four hour care and other specialized nursing services.

What questions should I ask to choose an appropriate facility?

- Can the facility meet my or my loved one's needs?
- Does it have a current state license?
- Does it accept Medicare and/or Medicaid?
- What problems were identified during the last survey or inspection? (A copy of the home's last inspection should be posted or available in the home.)
- Are the residents treated with dignity?
- Is the home clean and odor free?
- Is there an ombudsman who visits regularly?
- Talk to residents and family members. What comments do they have?

Try to visit several homes or facilities, more than once if possible, and at different times. You'll be able to see how staff interacts with residents at meal times and during afternoon or evening hours.

For a more complete checklist, contact your local Area Agency on Aging or the Missouri Long-Term Care Ombudsman Program at 1-800-309-3282 .

What should I look for when signing a long-term care facility contract?

Residents have rights secured by both state and federal laws (these rights are listed at the end of these questions). The admission agreement is also very important in defining a resident's rights and obligations.

Carefully read the admission agreement and ask questions when you don't understand something. The agreement must specify items and services included in the daily rate, and items and services not included.

It should also state how the facility handles emergency situations and when a resident may be transferred.

Each facility also has a "bed-hold policy" that specifies how residents can secure their bed, or a bed in the facility, if they have to go to the hospital.

The agreement must not require family members to be responsible for their loved one's bills if their loved ones receive Medicaid.

What happens if I run out of money?

Many people enter a skilled nursing or an intermediate care facility as private pay residents and turn to Medicaid when their money runs out. If the home is Medicaid-certified, it must continue to care for a resident who eventually requires Medicaid if a Medicaid bed is available. To ensure continued coverage, request a Medicaid-certified bed upon admission. If there is a suspected diagnosis of mental illness, mental retardation, or related disorder, a special screening process may be required.

Placement in a Medicaid bed allows a person to take advantage of the "division of assets" program. The program helps ensure residents' spouses who live in the community are not impoverished because of their loved one's facility bills. A person can apply for Medicaid at his or her local Division of Family Services office.

In some instances, residents are eligible for a cash grant to help cover the costs of their care. The grant, funded by Missouri tax dollars, is available to eligible low-income persons through application at their local Division of Family Services office.

What is the cost of facility care?

Nationwide, the cost is around is $64,000 per year for a skilled nursing home. The average cost in a residential care facility is around $24,000. When selecting a facility, find out which services are included in the basic daily charge and which are not covered. Ask whether a deposit is required and the procedure for return of the deposit. (Medicaid residents do not have to give a deposit).

Do all facilities accept Medicare and/or Medicaid reimbursement for care?

Many skilled nursing and intermediate care facilities accept Medicare and/or Medicaid reimbursement, but residential care facilities do not. However, residential care facility residents may be eligible for state assistance through the Supplemental Nursing Care grant. In addition residential care facilities may participate in the Medicaid Personal Care Program. The Personal Care Program offers Medicaid-eligible residents assistance with activities of daily living. This program provides residential care residents an alternative to nursing facility care.

What are my rights as a long-term care facility resident?

Missourians who live in a long-term care facility licensed

by the state are guaranteed certain rights under the Missouri Omnibus Nursing Home Act of 1979 and the federal Omnibus Budget Reconciliation Act of 1987. The rights are:

- You will be informed (at the time of admission to the facility and periodically during your stay) orally and in writing of your rights and responsibilities as a resident.
- You will be informed of the services available and related charges, including protection of personal funds if held by the facility, and all services not covered in the facility's daily rate.
- You may purchase or rent goods or services not included in the facility rate from a provider of your choice.
- You will receive notice before room or roommate changes are made.
- You may examine results of facility inspections including plans of correction.
- You have the right to receive service with reasonable accommodation of your individual needs and preferences except when your health and safety or that of other residents would be endangered.
- You have the right to not have your life regulated beyond what is necessary in providing resident services.
- You have the right to retain your personal possessions as space permits.
- You have the right to be informed of all aspects of your care, to choose your own personal physician, to participate in planning your care and treatment, including any changes in care and treatment. You have the right to refuse treatment and to be informed of the consequences of such refusal.
- You shall be encouraged and assisted throughout your stay to exercise your rights. You have the right to voice complaints and recommend changes regarding personal care, behavior of other residents, conditions in the facility, or other unmet needs or expectations and to expect

121

prompt efforts will be made to address complaints.

- You have a right to privacy for visits with your spouse and may share a room with your spouse if you are both residents and both agree to the cohabitation.
- You have the right to privacy and respect regarding accommodations, personal care, medical treatment, written and telephone communications and visits with other individuals.
- All information related to your medical, personal, social, or financial affairs will be kept confidential.
- You may be discharged or transferred only for medical reasons, for your own welfare or that of others, or for nonpayment. Pre-transfer and pre-discharge notices must be made at least thirty days in advance. Written notices must go to the resident, family member or legal representative or long-term care ombudsman if there is no family and include reasons for the action, the right to appeal and information on how to contact the State Long-Term Care Ombudsman. The facility must assist you in arranging other accommodations.
- You have the right to participate in resident councils and your family has the right to meet together in the facility with families of other residents.
- You may associate and communicate privately with persons of your choice. You may have free access to an ombudsman, your individual physician, or any representative of the state or federal government.
- You have the right to have appropriate activities for your participation and may engage in social, religious and community activities of your choice.
- You have the right to be free from physical or mental abuse, corporal punishment, involuntary seclusion and any physical or chemical restraints imposed for purposes of discipline or for convenience of the staff. Restraints may not be used except under the direction of a physician and only to treat your medical symptoms.

Listed below are definitions from the same dhss web site:

Level of Licensure:

Intermediate Care Facility (ICF): Premises utilized by an owner, operator, or manager to provide twenty-four hour accommodation, board, personal care, and basic health and nursing care services under the daily supervision of a licensed nurse and direction of a licensed physician to three or more residents dependent for care and supervision.

Nursing Facility (NF): A federal term used to identify a facility certified under Medicaid. The facility may be an intermediate care or a skilled nursing facility.

Residential Care Facility I (RCF I): Premises utilized by an owner, operator or manager to provide twenty-four hour care to three or more residents who need or are provided with shelter, board, and protective oversight, which may include storage, distribution or administration of medications and care during short-term illness or recuperation.

Residential Care Facility II (RCF II): Premises utilized by an owner, operator, or manager to provide twenty-four hour accommodation, board, and care to three or more residents who need or are provided with supervision of diets, assistance in personal care, storage, distribution or administration of medications, supervision of health care under the direction of a licensed physician, and protective oversight, including care during short-term illness or recuperation.

Skilled Nursing Facility (SNF): Premises utilized by an owner, operator or manager to provide for twenty-four hour accommodation, board and skilled nursing care and treatment services to at least three residents. Skilled nursing care and treatment services are commonly performed by or under the supervision of a registered professional nurse for individuals requiring twenty-four hour care by licensed nursing personnel including acts of observation, care and counsel of the aged, ill, injured or infirm, the administration of medications and treatments as prescribed by a licensed physician or dentist, and other nursing functions requiring substantial specialized judgment and skill.

The following nursing home checklist was downloaded from: www.medicare.gov/nursing/checklist.asp.

Nursing Homes
Nursing Home Checklist

Checklists can help you evaluate the nursing homes that you call or visit. Use a new checklist for each home you call or visit. Then, compare the scores. This will help you select a nursing home that is a good choice for you or your relative.

Nursing Home Name: _____

Date Visited: _____

Address: _____

I. Basic Information:

    1. Is the facility Medicare certified?   Yes   No

    2. Is the facility Medicaid certified?   Yes   No

    3. Is this a skilled nursing facility?   Yes   No

    4. Is the facility accepting new patients?   Yes   No

    5. Is there a waiting period for admission?   Yes   No

    6. Is a skilled bed available to you?   Yes   No

Useful Tips

- Generally, skilled nursing care is available only for a short period of time after a hospitalization. Custodial

care is for a much longer period of time. If a facility offers both types of care, learn if residents may transfer
between levels of care within the nursing home without
having to move from their old room or from the nursing
home.

- Nursing homes that only take Medicaid residents might
offer longer term but less intensive levels of care. Nursing Homes that don't accept Medicaid payment may
make a resident move when Medicare or the resident's
own money runs out.

- An occupancy rate is the total number of residents currently living in a nursing home divided by the home's
total number of beds. Occupancy rates vary by area,
depending on the overall number of available nursing
home beds.

II. Nursing Home Information:

1. Is the home and the current administrator licensed?
                    Yes   No
2. Does the home conduct background checks on all
staff?   Yes   No
3. Does the home have special services units?
                    Yes   No
4. Does the home have abuse prevention training?
                    Yes   No

Useful Tips

- **Licensure:** The nursing home and its administrator
should be licensed by the State to operate.

- **Background Checks**: Do the nursing home's procedures
to screen potential employees for a history of abuse meet
your State's requirements? Your State's Ombudsman
program might be able to help you with this information.

- **Special Services**: Some nursing homes have special service units like rehabilitation, Alzheimer's, and hospice. Learn if there are separate waiting periods or facility guidelines for when residents would be moved on or off the special unit.

- **Staff Training**: Do the nursing home's training programs educate employees about how to recognize resident abuse and neglect, how to deal with aggressive or difficult residents, and how to deal with the stress of caring for so many needs? Are there clear procedures to identify events or trends that might lead to abuse and neglect, and on how to investigate, report, and resolve your complaints?
- **Loss Prevention**: Are there policies or procedures to safeguard resident possessions?

For Sections III through VI, give the nursing home a grade from one to five. One is worst, five is best.

III. Quality of Life:

	Worst			Best	
1. Residents can make choices about their daily routine. Examples are when to go to bed or get up, when to bathe, or when to eat.	1	2	3	4	5
2. The interaction between staff and patient is warm and respectful.	1	2	3	4	5
3. The home is easy to visit for friends and family.	1	2	3	4	5
4. The nursing home meets your cultural, religious, or language needs.	1	2	3	4	5
5. The nursing home smells and looks clean and has good lighting.	1	2	3	4	5

	Worst				Best
6. The home maintains comfortable temperatures.	1	2	3	4	5
7. The resident rooms have personal articles and furniture.	1	2	3	4	5
8. The public and resident rooms have comfortable furniture.	1	2	3	4	5
9. The nursing home and its dining room are generally quiet.	1	2	3	4	5
10. Residents may choose from a variety of activities that they like.	1	2	3	4	5
11. The nursing home has outside volunteer groups.	1	2	3	4	5
12. The nursing home has outdoor areas for resident use and helps residents to get outside.	1	2	3	4	5

TOTAL: _____

(Best Possible Score: 60)

IV. of Care:

	Worst				Best
1. The facility corrected any Quality of Care deficiencies that were in the State inspection report.	1	2	3	4	5
2. Residents may continue to see their personal physician.	1	2	3	4	5
3. Residents are clean, appropriately dressed, and well groomed.	1	2	3	4	5
4. Nursing Home staff respond quickly to requests for help.	1	2	3	4	5
5. The administrator and staff	1	2	3	4	5

127

seem comfortable with each other and with the residents.

	Worst				Best
6. Residents have the same care givers on a daily basis.	1	2	3	4	5
7. There are enough staff at night and on week-ends or holidays to care for each resident.	1	2	3	4	5
8. The home has an arrangement for emergency situations with a nearby hospital.	1	2	3	4	5
9. The family and residents councils are independent from the nursing home's management.	1	2	3	4	5
10. Care plan meetings are held at times that are easy for residents and their family members to attend.	1	2	3	4	5

TOTAL: _____

(Best Possible Score: 50)

Useful Tips

• Good care plans are essential to good care. They should be put together by a team of providers and family and updated as often as necessary.

V. Nutrition and Hydration (Diet and Fluids):

	Worst				Best
1. The home corrected any deficiencies in these areas that were on the recent state inspection report.	1	2	3	4	5
2. There are enough staff to assist each resident who requires help with eating.	1	2	3	4	5

128

	Worst				Best
3. The food smells and looks good and is served at proper temperatures.	1	2	3	4	5
4. Residents are offered choices of food at mealtimes.	1	2	3	4	5
5. Residents' weight is routinely monitored.	1	2	3	4	5
6. There are water pitchers and glasses on tables in the rooms.	1	2	3	4	5
7. Staff help residents drink if they are not able to do so on their own.	1	2	3	4	5
8. Nutritious snacks are available during the day and evening.	1	2	3	4	5
9. The environment in the dining room encourages residents to relax, socialize, and enjoy their food.	1	2	3	4	5

TOTAL: _____

(Best Possible Score: 45)

Useful Tips

- Ask the professional staff how the medicine a resident takes can affect what they eat and how often they may want something to drink.
- Visit at mealtime. Are residents rushed through meals or do they have time to finish eating and to use the meal as an opportunity to socialize with each other?
- Sometimes the food a home serves is fine, but a resident still won't eat. Nursing home residents may like some control over their diet. Can they select their meals from a menu or select their mealtime?
- If residents need help eating, do care plans specify what

type of assistance they will receive?

VI. Safety	Worst				Best
1. There are handrails in the hallways and grab bars in the bathrooms.	1	2	3	4	5
2. Exits are clearly marked.	1	2	3	4	5
3. Spills and other accidents are cleaned up quickly.	1	2	3	4	5
4. Hallways are free of clutter and have good lighting.	1	2	3	4	5
5. There are enough staff to help move residents quickly in an emergency.	1	2	3	4	5
6. The nursing home has smoke detectors and sprinklers.	1	2	3	4	5

TOTAL: _____

(Best Possible Score: 30)

Useful Tips Relating to Information in Nursing Home Compare

- Nursing Home Compare contains summary information about nursing homes from their last state inspection. It also contains information that was reported by the nursing homes prior to the last State inspection including nursing home and resident characteristics. If you have questions or concerns about the information on a nursing home, you should discuss them during your visit. This section contains useful tips and questions that you may want to ask the nursing home staff, family members and residents of the nursing home during your visit.

Nursing Home Compare Information on Results of Nursing Home Inspections

- Bring a copy of the Nursing Home Compare inspection results for the nursing home. Ask whether the deficiencies have been corrected.
- Ask to see a copy of the most recent nursing home inspection report.

Nursing Home Compare Information on Resident and Nursing Home Characteristics

1. Residents with Physical Restraints

- Does it appear that there is sufficient staff to assist residents who need help in moving or getting in and out of chairs and bed?
- Ask the Director of Nursing who is involved in the decisions about physical restraints.
- When physical restraints are used, do the staff remove the physical restraints on a regular basis to help residents with moving, and with activities of daily living?
- Do the staff help residents with physical restraints to get in and out of bed and chairs when they want to get up?
- Do staff help residents with physical restraints to move as much as they would like to?

2. Residents with Pressure (Bed) Sores

- Ask the staff how they identify if a resident is at risk for skin breakdown. Ask them what they do to prevent pressure sores for these residents.
- Ask the staff about the percentage of their residents that have pressure sores and why.
- Do you see staff helping residents change their positions in wheelchairs, chairs, and beds?

131

3. Residents with Bowel and Bladder Incontinence
- Does the nursing home smell clean?
- Ask the staff what steps they take to prevent bowel and bladder incontinence for residents who are at risk.

4. Residents Who Are Very Dependent in Eating
- Look at your response to Question 2 in Section V above.
- Observe residents who need help in eating. Are they able to finish their meals or is the food returned to the kitchen uneaten?

5. Residents Who Are Bedfast
- Ask the Director of Nursing how staff are assigned to care for these residents.

6. Residents With Restricted Joint Motion
- Ask the Director of Nursing how the nursing home cares for residents with restricted joint motion.
- Do the residents get help with getting out of chairs and beds when they want to get up?

7. Residents with Unplanned Weight Gain or Loss
- Look at your responses to Questions 2, 3, 4, 5, 8, and 9 in section V above.

8. Residents with Behavioral Symptoms
- What management and/or medical approaches for behavioral symptoms are being used by the nursing home?
- How does staff handle residents that have behavioral symptoms such as calling out or yelling?
- Ask whether residents with behavioral symptoms are checked by a doctor or behavioral specialist.
- Ask whether staff get special training to help them to provide care to residents with behavioral symptoms.
- Nursing Home Compare Information on Nursing Staff

Caring, competent nursing staff who respect each resident and family member are very important in assuring that residents get needed care and enjoy the best possible quality of life. Adequate nursing staff is needed to assess resident needs, plan and give them care, and help them with eating, bathing and other activities. Some residents (e.g., those who are more dependent in eating or who are bedfast) need more help than other residents depending on their conditions.

The combinations of registered nurses (RNs), licensed practical and vocational nurses (LPNs/LVNs), and certified nursing assistants (CNAs) that nursing homes may have vary depending on the type of care that residents need and the number of residents in the nursing home.

- Look at your responses to Questions 2 and 5 in section III above and Questions 4, 5, and 10 in section IV above. Also look at your responses to Questions 2 and 7 in section V above.
- Are nursing staff members courteous and friendly to residents and to other staff?
- Do nursing staff respond timely to residents calls for assistance such as help getting in and out of bed, dressing and going to the bathroom?
- Observe meal times. Do all residents who need assistance with eating get help? Do staff give each resident enough time to chew food thoroughly and complete the meal?
- Which nursing staff members are involved in planning the residents individual care? (Are they the same ones who give the care to residents?)
- Ask questions about staff turnover. Is there frequent turnover among certified nursing assistants (CNAs)? What about nurses and supervisors, including the Director of Nursing and the Administrator? If staff changes frequently, ask why.

- While the number of nursing staff is important to good care, also consider other factors, such as education and training. How many registered nurses (RNs) are on the staff, and how many available on each shift? What kind of training do certified nursing assistants (CNAs) receive? How does the nursing home ensure that all staff receive continuing education and keep their knowledge and skills up-to-date?

There is pdf format form you can download as well at:
www.medicare.gov/nursing/checklist.pdf

Eric's Comments

In a town 90 miles from us, the Anderson Guest Home for the mentally disabled was destroyed by fire, killing ten residents and a care worker. According to news reports, there was a short in the wiring. The news reported that there were no sprinklers. State law at that time did not require sprinklers. The group home housed mentally challenged individuals receiving Medicaid benefits in Missouri. The responses to this tragedy will be multiple and are already beginning. There will be lawsuits, possibly some form of criminal action, new laws passed, investigations by the governor, continued media reporting, etc. All of this is okay but it doesn't and won't fix the problem.

We should never leave a loved one in any type of shelter or living arrangement that is unsafe. Ultimately, only the power of the consumer can fix these types of problems. When you are involved in seeking a shelter, nursing home, assisted living, retirement living, or any other type of place for your loved one, for God's sake, go in with your eyes, ears, nose and brain working. You can see whether there are sprinklers, smoke detectors, adequate staff and a safe, clean environment. If the place doesn't seem okay, don't trust them with your loved one. The guilt you may feel for the rest of your life from putting your loved one in harm's way, even unintentionally, will be far greater than the short-term frustration in finding a safe place now. It is absurd to believe that either the State or Federal Government can care for the elderly better than families or friends. If bureaucratic care is the only answer, we need to insist on a quality place for that care. CASA (Court Appointed Special Advocates) was created to represent children in the child welfare system. We probably need to create a watchdog group for our elderly.

I believe our bureaucracy has impersonalized our end-of-life decisions. I believe we all need to know our options and make decisions based on our own desires, needs, wants and wishes. We seem to enter most of these crucial decision-making times with other people trying to decide what is best for us. That's great as long as they keep us in mind! The health care bureaucracy is the method most elderly people turn to as they age. It's natural because illness or injury thrusts the elderly into the health care bureaucracy. This is necessary but the forces of health care can then take over. Pretty soon, we have visiting nurses, therapy and anything else Medicare will cover. These agencies add input into how we should live. We get a sterile evaluation of what someone else thinks is best for us. What about our quality of life? I don't think it is always considered. With some bureaucracies, I believe it is quality of life as they determine it to be.

When alternative living arrangements are to be made, first be sure your elderly loved one has their own doctor. Regardless of the facility they enter, be sure your doctor can remain in control. The Missouri Omnibus Nursing Home Act of 1979 and the Federal Omnibus Budget Reconciliation Act of 1987 established that you, or your elderly loved one, may choose your own physician. When Mom was in a skilled nursing facility, they didn't tell me this. They wouldn't take orders from her doctor or allow him to provide care. We had to use their doctor. Of course, we moved her back to her home so it didn't matter in the long run; only I wish I'd have known then what I know now!   When you visit a nursing home be sure of the services provided. I have the following suggestions:

1. Tour the facility with your eyes open.
2. See what services are offered and if there is adequate help for these services?
3. Meal time is a good time to see how much help there is and how helpful the staff is.
4. How clean is the facility?
5. How clean is the kitchen? Look not only at meal time but at other times as well.
6. How clean is the eating area? I've seen places where trays and tables are not wiped or clean.
7. How many call lights do you see on?
8. How long do people have to wait for simple creature comforts such as a drink of water or for help to the bathroom?
9. How is the ease of access, getting in and out? This includes to the facility, their rooms, the bathroom and shower, and eating and recreational areas.
10. If this is a retirement living facility, is there ease of access (same as #9 above) and parking for their personal vehicle?
11. What type of transportation do they provide?
12. What other type of transportation is available?
13. How does the place smell?
14. What is the employee to patient ratio? (This number can vary depending on the level of care of the facility and the only standards I could find had to do with fire safety).
15. Would you personally live there?

18.
How Do We Pay the Bills?

The nationwide average yearly cost for nursing home care is $64,000 per person according to the Department of Health and Senior Services. Locally the average cost is $45,000 per person per year. The majority of us will pay for this expense from our own funds. How will we do this? Some hope to pay with long-term care insurance. I have downloaded the following material from A/PACT.

Aging Parents and Adult Children Together (A/PACT)

LONG-TERM CARE INSURANCE

(Fifth in a 10-part series)

At ages 59 and 61, your parents are independent and self-sufficient. Still, they realize that an accident, sudden illness or simple aging could trigger the need for long-term care. They nursed your grandmother through her 10-year bout with Alzheimer's and are well aware that a loved one's illness can cause heartbreak and financial strain for the entire family. Can a long-term care insurance policy for your parents help protect everyone concerned?

As the senior population grows and health care costs escalate, adult children are becoming increasingly concerned about caring for their aging parents. Many families are dealing with the challenges of mental or physical disability or prolonged illness. For thousands of others, these realities may be just around the corner.

The challenge for these families is to provide the best possible long-term care for a parent without causing severe financial hardship for the rest of the family. In most cases, families must plan ahead without knowing the answers to key questions: Will a parent need round-the-clock nursing home care or assistance with daily activities such as bathing and dressing? Will home health care be enough? Will Medicare pay for it? Does the parent qualify for Medicaid? What cost will the family incur?

One thing is certain — long-term care is very expensive. Unlike traditional medical care, which seeks to rehabilitate or correct certain medical ills, long-term care aims to help people with chronic conditions compensate for limitations on their ability to function independently. Long-term care involves a wide variety of services and, generally, older people often need more care than they anticipate.

Government assistance programs may offer little help. Medicare — the federal health insurance program for people over the age of 65 — provides very limited long-term care benefits and can require substantial co-payments. Medicaid — the public health care program for low-income Americans — has strict financial eligibility criteria and generally requires beneficiaries to deplete their savings, or "spend down," before it will pay for services. Other public services may be available but typically are offered on a sliding-fee scale, based on ability to pay. There also may be waiting lists.

While long-term care insurance is not for everyone, it is an attractive form of security for many people. Depending on the policy, long-term care insurance can cover nursing home stays, home health care and community-based services.

People usually buy long-term care policies from private insurance companies. However, a growing number of employers are now offering policies to their employees, employees' parents and retirees.

Policies vary widely in coverage and cost. Some only cover nursing home care; others only home care. Shop around and consider the following factors before buying a policy:

- The age, health, overall retirement objectives and financial resources of the person who is to be insured;
- The financial stability of the insurance companies you're considering; and,
- The "triggers" each company requires to start coverage.

Existing health problems, such as Parkinson's or Alzheimer's, might prevent some people from obtaining long-term care insurance due to medical underwriting standards that insurance companies use to keep their rates affordable. Without such provisions, most people would not buy coverage until they needed services.

For More Information

While buying long-term care insurance can be an intimidating process, state insurance departments and senior counseling programs can help.

Health Insurance Information, Counseling and Assistance Program (HIICAP)
National Association of Insurance Commissioners
P.O. Box 87-7870
Kansas City, MO 64187-7870
(816) 374-7259; fax: (816) 471-7004

NAIC publishes A Shopper's Guide to Long-Term Care Insurance, containing information on all aspects of long-term care insurance and the addresses and telephone numbers for every state insurance department, agency on aging and insurance counseling program.

United Seniors Health Cooperative
409 Third Street, SW
Second Floor
Washington, DC 20024-3212
(800) 637-2604
USHC publishes Long-Term Care Planning: A Dollar & Sense Guide.

American Association of Retired Persons
Fulfillment
601 E Street, NW
Washington, DC 20049
AARP publishes, Before You Buy — A Guide to Long-Term Care Insurance, Stock No. D12893.
Prepared by the National Association of Insurance Commissioners

Eric's Comments

If your elderly loved one does not have this insurance it is too late for them. This section may be relevant for you. I haven't done a lot of research on this topic and have had difficulty in learning just what specific policies will cover. Be wary of the "medically necessary" stipulations required for coverage. Most policies I've reviewed pay for medically necessary expenses which Medicare generally covers as well. The funny thing is; eating, safe and clean living surroundings, trips to the store or doctor aren't medically necessary. Try living without them. I know elderly who have purchased policies believing they will pay for helping them stay home. The bulk of time spent in helping the elderly people stay home has nothing to do with medically necessary needs or health care. Be sure what is covered here! Probably, consulting with a financial planner is good advice for Boomers or younger adults.

Aging Parents and Adult Children Together (A/PACT)

THE THREE MEDI'S: MEDICARE, MEDIGAP AND MEDICAID

(Seventh in a 10-part series)

Your Mom is turning 65. She will be receiving Social Security retirement benefits but is very concerned about how to finance her health care. She owns her home, has a limited pension, and with Social Security, will be able to make ends meet but with little money to spare. Will she be eligible for Medicare? Does she need Medigap insurance? Can Medicaid help?

Medicare is the national health insurance program for Social Security recipients who are over 65 or permanently disabled. It is administered by the federal Health Care Financing Administration. Private insurance companies contract with the government to make payments to medical providers.

Medicare is not a welfare program. That is, personal income and assets are not considered in determining an individual's eligibility or benefits. Medicare coverage is similar to the coverage that private insurance companies offer: Medicare pays a portion of the cost of some medical care and the beneficiary — the patient — assumes the cost of deductibles and the co-payments to healthcare providers.

141

Medicare has two coverage components — *Part A and Part B*. *Part A* covers in-patient hospital care, hospice care, in-patient care in a skilled nursing facility, and home health care services. *Part B* covers medical care and services provided by doctors and other medical practitioners, durable medical equipment and some outpatient care and home health care services. *Part A* is financed mostly through federal payroll taxes; the majority of beneficiaries do not pay a premium for this coverage. *Part B* is financed through monthly premiums paid by beneficiaries who choose this coverage and by general revenues from the federal government. Beneficiaries may be required to pay deductibles and make co-payments under both *Part A* and *Part B*.

Medicare recipients can choose to receive their health care services through Medicare's traditional *fee-for-service* system or through *managed care plans*. The fee-for-service system lets patients see any physician who participates in Medicare. Although generally less expensive, managed care plans limit patients to certain doctors and generally require patients to get referrals to specialists from their managed care plan physicians, who may be known as *gatekeepers*. Some Medicare managed care plans let beneficiaries see a specialist without prior approval, but they charge a premium for that. Generally, beneficiaries who choose a managed care Medicare plan must get all their care through the plan to receive coverage.

Beginning January 1, 1999, Medicare recipients will have additional options for financing their health care coverage under a new *Part C* of Medicare. Also known as *Medicare+Choice, Part C* options will include *coordinated-care plans*, *Medical Savings Accounts*, and *private fee-for-service* plans. Beneficiaries will not have to change their current Medicare arrangement, however, and should do so only after study and thought.

Medicare Supplemental Insurance — also known as *Medigap* — can help beneficiaries pay for medical care that Medicare does not cover, including deductibles and co-payments. While all Medigap policies must contain basic or "core" benefits, beneficiaries can get additional benefits for higher premiums.

In deciding whether Medigap or supplemental insurance makes sense for your parent, consider your parent's current health status and likely future medical needs (as best you can) as well as the policy's cost and any restrictions, such as benefit restrictions for pre-existing conditions. Also check for restrictions on the policyholder's ability to switch from one policy to another. Before enrolling in any insurance company, check with the insurance commissioner in your parent's home state to see if there are unresolved complaints against the company on file.

Medicaid is different. Based on need, it helps pay the medical care for low-income older or disabled people and other individuals, including some with moderate incomes but high health care expenses. Eligibility for Medicaid is based on an applicant's income and assets. Medicaid is financed jointly by federal and state governments and, while each state must follow basic eligibility and benefit requirements, significant details vary among states.

Medicaid covers far more nursing home care than Medicare, and pays for custodial and skilled care. It doesn't limit the time a beneficiary can stay in a nursing home or other care facility.

Both Medicare and Medicaid can be a source of funding for long-term home health care, but Medicare covers home health care only if the person is homebound and needs skilled nursing or therapy services.

To apply for Medicare, your parents should contact the nearest Medicare office in their state about three months before their 65th birthday. Those who are receiving Social Security disability benefits also should inquire about Medicare. For more information, contact the Social Security Administration at (800) 772-1213, or the Health Care Financing Administration at (800) 638-6833, *www.hcfa.gov.* HCFA publishes the *1997 Guide to Health Insurance for People with Medicare*, Pub. No. HCFA-02110. For Medicaid information, contact the state medical assistance office, often called the State Department of Social Services or Department of Human Services.

For More Information
The Center for Medicare Advocacy, Inc., publishes a variety of materials on Medicare, Medigap and Medicaid, including items on how to pursue a Medicare appeal or home health care appeal.

Center for Medicare Advocacy, Inc.
P.O. Box 350
Willimantic, CT 06226
(860) 456-7790.

Health Insurance Information, Counseling and Assistance Program (HIICAP)
National Academy of Elder Law Attorneys, Inc. (NAELA)
1604 N. Country Club Road
Tucson, AZ 85716-4005
(520) 881-4005; fax: (520) 325-7925

American Bar Association Commission on Legal Problems of the Elderly
740 15th Street, NW
Washington, DC 20005-1022
(202) 662-8690; fax: (202) 662-8698

The Commission publishes The ABA Legal Guide for Older Americans, which includes information about consumer legal issues. The cost is $13.00.

The Medicare Hotline at 1-800-638-6833

Prepared by the Center for Medicare Advocacy

Eric's Comments

It is important that you know what financial programs are available for your parents or elderly loved one. The programs discussed above now also include Medicare Part D prescription drug coverage. Income and net worth are factors in all these programs. Most of us will have all the Medicare coverage available. We will have to cover non-medically necessary personal expenses out of our own pockets. These expenses may include meal preparation, bathing, housekeeping and transportation for errands or a variety of other non-medical expenses. This happens until either you die or run out of money or Medicaid takes over.

There have been some recent changes to the Medicaid qualifications pertaining to assets and personal property. Medicaid will pay for some non-medical expenses to help the elderly stay homes. Medicaid programs recognize it is less expensive and better for the elderly to remain in their own home. This may be different in various states. To qualify for Medicaid, monthly income and assets much be low enough and, I believe, the home is excluded until death. It's important for you to find out all the facts about Medicaid. The state actually will be listed as a remainder beneficiary on annuities and other properties. We see examples of people trying to pass on their assets to their children to protect the children's inheritance.

While I'm in favor of the elderly trying to protect their children's inheritance, it doesn't make lot of sense for our society to allow people to protect their assets and then be "wards" of the state. We should use our money and what we've accumulated for our own well-being. If I can give my money, land or valuables to my children in advance and then have the state take care of me, it somehow seems wrong. That means ultimately the state is providing my child's inheritance. Believe me; my quality of life should *not* be in the hands of the state. My children would rather see me happy than have my money in the first place. Most kids would agree. If your children's inheritance is their major priority, then the relationship has a problem. I'm making my will whereby my heirs must follow my advance directive and wishes or their share of the estate will go to charity.

I just read an article by Bob O'Toole, (Inside GCM Co-Editor) titled, "Major Implications on How Americans Must Plan to Pay for Long-term Care."

According to O'Toole's article, currently Medicaid pays the nursing home bills of twelve million elderly and disabled people. The article states that the Deficit Reduction Act drastically and suddenly changes the way that long-term care, especially nursing home care, will be paid for by many families. The National Academy of Elder Law Attorneys issued a statement saying that the Deficit Reduction Act creates, "A health care crisis of unprecedented magnitude for our most vulnerable citizens." According to NAEL Attorney Jeffrey A. Marshall, CELA, elders will have to cope with provisions that attempt to shift more of the financial burden of nursing home care onto families and nursing facilities.

> "Few seniors have insurance that covers long-term care and most nursing home residents rely on Medicaid to cover part of the cost of their care. The new law will make it more difficult for these residents to obtain this financial aid."

Under prior law, an individual making a financial gift could be ineligible for Medicaid-paid nursing home care for up to 3 years from the date of making the gift. The Deficit Reduction Act changes the start of the penalty period for transferred assets from the date of the transfer to the date of Medicaid application. This means that the penalty period will not start until the individual is in a nursing home and is out of other funds to pay for care. The law also extends the look-back time to five years. According to Marshall and several other published comments of elder law attorneys , "The grandparent who helped pay for a grandchild's education, the parent who helps a child with medical bills, and even the family farmer who passes on the farm will all be caught by this law if they get sick within 5 years of making the gift.

From my perspective, this is long overdue. Why should I, as a taxpayer, be responsible for someone who gives their resources away to avoid paying for their own care? Under the previous sentimental statements, the grandparent, parent or farmer who is supposedly doing such noble things is, in the end, asking the state or taxpayers to be responsible. If we can get it through our heads that we are responsible for our own well-being, we will be better off at the end of our lives. Our entire family should want us to spend our resources on ourselves first and live in our own homes as independently as possible.

You could make an example of a person with $1,000,000 in cash and assets. The average cost of nursing home care in the U.S. is estimated to be $64,000. In our area, it is $45,000. If you divide the assets by the estimated cost, you would find out that this person could pay for their nursing home services for 15 years and 8 months; if the assets didn't earn any interest or dividends the entire period of time. Why should this hypothetical person be allowed to "gift away" their money and assets to avoid paying for their end-of-life care? Why should we as taxpayers think somehow this is fair? Fair for whom? We would all be better off to figure out whose money it is and see to it that it benefits the person who has it.

When you talk to elders, you pick up this sense that they don't mind suffering so their kids can have their assets to enjoy a better life. I disagree. Many adult children wouldn't want their parents to do without or suffer. Most kids wouldn't want their parent in a nursing home if they truly understood their parent's wishes. The lesson here is, apply all *their* resources toward *their* end-of-life wishes.

19.
Assisted Living At Home:
Why Pay More?

There are several websites that assess when one's needs have changed and care is necessary. I believe in "thinking ahead of disaster." The earlier we start implementing preventive changes and improvements for our personal well- being and home safety, the longer we will remain independent. The nationwide average cost for rest home care is $64,000 per person according to the Department of Health and Senior Services. Locally the average cost is over $45,000 per person. The majority of us will pay for this expense from our own funds. With the proper planning and forethought, we should be able to stay in our own homes for less money. It is far less expensive to prevent a fall than to treat the resulting injuries. Typically, people desire to remain in their homes as long as they are able.

Once the decision has been made to remain home, the next question is "How do we find the best person to help with care at the most affordable prices?" Some families try to hire the caregivers themselves.

There is a lot more to this than you may think. You would become this individual's employer. There are many business transactions and financial issues involved when you become an employer. The following actions are required: Withholding social security and Medicare payments, withholding federal and state income taxes, paying the employer's matching share of social security and Medicare payments, paying Federal Unemployment Taxes and

State Unemployment taxes, providing workers compensation insurance, filing required periodic payroll reports, and furnishing year-end wage reports. There also is a problem with work schedules and filling needs if the caregiver is unable to work.

A reputable professional agency will provide all these services. The agency will also advertise for, screen, interview and reference-check each candidate. Our agency, Assisting Aging Parents, checks driving records and criminal record screenings, checks the Missouri Employee Disqualification list and the State's Family Care Registry as well. If you decide to use a health care provider. they must verify the employee's licenses.

Our local home health care agencies provide non-medical personal services as well as medically necessary services. Many of the medically based agencies refer to the non-medical care as "custodial services." My temporary employment agency supplied supplemental staffing to one such local agency. As I visited with the owner, I was led to believe that the non-medical services were quite a nuisance to them. In almost every meeting with them, they complained about this part of their medically based, nursed owned business.

As I entered the local marketplace to provide non-medical custodial services, I thought I would be welcomed with open arms. After all, I was going to take over a share of the market that bothered them continually and surely didn't make them as much money as the medical portion of their business.

My business provides non-medical personal and custodial services designed to help people stay in their homes at affordable prices. My driving force is helping people stay home, if it is right for them. I provide an option to health care providers. My basic rates for our services are on average 30% less than if they were provided by a health care provider. These are the same services, same employee qualifications, same employee candidate base, and same employee pay. I see ads about nurse owned or hospital owned home health agencies. Watch out! Obviously, to share an expression, "They have a dog in the hunt." Their viewpoint is vastly different from mine or a Care Manager. Health care providers say it is the patient that counts, but is it?

The most important piece of our health care puzzle is a doctor. We need to communicate to our doctor exactly how we want to be treated. Our doctor needs to clearly understand our end-of-life wishes and be an advocate for us. In our area there are over a thousand doctors but very few who specialize in Geriatric Medicine. In the future, we need to develop groups of doctors that are dedicated to keeping us at home.

When we enter elder health care through home health agencies, the agency evaluates, sets up, recommends, etc., our care. They will even make a care plan, yet they must ultimately have a doctor's orders to really do anything. No medication or treatment, etc., will be administered, other than perhaps emergency or first aid services, without a doctor's orders and supervision. Nurse Practitioners may also treat and prescribe with a doctor's oversight.

I believe that entering health care through a home health agency run by nurses is similar to going to an automobile agency and trying to get the best deal to buy a car from a mechanic or the service manager. While they may be very knowledgeable, they don't make the decisions. With some bureaucracies, I believe it is the quality of life as *they* determine it to be. When do you remember the medical community being concerned with your pocket book? As we move forward we clearly need to separate home care from health care. Cooking, cleaning and driving do not require an R.N. or M.D.!

Perceptions of Experts

A number of year ago I was invited to the Christmas party and banquet for a local health care clinic. The event was held in the newest, most prestigious hotel in our town. The decorations were superb. There was a band providing lively entertainment. Drinks were flowing from the complementary bar, and everyone was decked out in their Christmas finest. It almost seemed like a segment from "The Lifestyles of the Rich and Famous."

We drank, danced, and hobnobbed with the high snobs. You could tell everybody was feeling pretty good about themselves. What a great impression by the clinic, to host such a wonderful event for their people.

We were seated at elegantly decorated tables of eight which had the finest china the hotel had to offer, along with festive table linens and Christmas theme center pieces. The silverware was perfectly placed, as well as the wine glasses and coffee cups with all the elegance available for a formal evening in Springfield, Missouri. What an experience! Christmas was definitely in the air! We heard the opening introductions, the glowing Christmas wishes and the elegant prayer. Finally, it was time to eat.

We started with a beautiful plate of greens (most of us think of this as a salad). It was dressed with some sort of tart vinaigrette dressing. The dressing seemed to contain no salt, sugar, or other potential harmful dietary substances. Quite frankly, it was terrible. At our table everyone seemed unanimous on the fact that it was almost not edible. Oh well, it was, after all, only the salad. Surely, in the most elegant of places, on the most festive of occasions, we were in for a rare and exquisite culinary treat to come.

We were served baked chicken breast with potato and vegetable medley. Sounds okay; looks okay; wait until you taste it. The chicken breast had the skin removed and was baked with virtually no spice, no salt, no fat, no lard, no skin, no seasoning, no taste! The vegetables were steamed, however, with no harmful flavoring added as well, and nobody knew how the potatoes were prepared. The meal was undoubtedly the healthiest meal that could be prepared. No salt! No sugar! No fat! Plenty of veggies, chicken, and a starch. Wow, a dietary work of art. It was terrible!

Virtually everyone there commented on the terrible meal; doctors, administrators, health care providers, everyone except the dieticians agreed. What a holiday disaster. No telling how much was spent on the celebration. What a dud!

After twenty-five years, I still remember this as the number one worst meal I ever tried to eat. What went wrong? How could such a disaster occur, especially at Christmas? After all, Christmas is a time for the child in all of us to return. Fudge, cookies and milk, food to excess, a time for festivals.

I asked the question, "Who planned the menu?" The answer was the health care dietary department (the experts). It might have been okay if this were a cholesterol convention, a health fair retreat, or an overeater's anonymous dinner. It was, however, a Christmas celebration! If you take notice, the best eating events are planned by people who like to eat. It is a simple fact. If food is involved, let the fat people plan the menu. "Do you want the experts planning your personal care?

When feeding my slightly-built father toward the end of his life, my sister would fix tofu and healthy foods. She had been a marathon runner and, to this day, observes a very healthy runner's diet. I was always the most overweight of my siblings. My father's perception of me was that of a "fat child." After a few tofu meals, my Dad (at only 130 pounds) requested that "I keep bringing the food." Sometimes it is good to have a "fat child."

153

20.
Protecting Seniors From Fraud

I have downloaded the following information from A/PACT.

Aging Parents and Adult Children Together (A/PACT)

CONSUMER FRAUD AGAINST THE ELDERLY

(First in a 10-part series)

During a visit with your mother, you notice a stack of wire transfer receipts totaling more than $65,000. When you ask what they're for, she says she's investing in a new hi-tech company. After you investigate further, you think she's being scammed by fraudulent telemarketers. What can you do?

Consumers lose more than $40 billion a year to telemarketing fraud. People over 50 years of age are especially vulnerable and account for about 56 percent of all victims, according to a recent study by the American Association of Retired Persons. Scam artists often target older people, knowing they tend to be trusting and polite toward strangers and are likely to be home and have time to talk with callers.

You can help empower your parents and others who may be targets of fraudulent telemarketers by describing some tip-offs to rip-offs, letting them know their rights and suggesting ways they can protect themselves.

Tip-Offs to Phone Fraud

Many scams involve bogus prize offers, phony travel packages, get-rich-quick investments and fake charities. Con artists are skilled liars who spend a lot of time polishing their sales pitches. As a result, it can be difficult to see through their scams.

Alert those you care about to be on their guard if they hear the buzz words for fraud. Among the tip-offs are:

- You must act "now" or the offer will expire.
- You've won a "free" gift, vacation or prize — but you must pay for "postage and handling" or some other charge.
- You must send money, give a credit card or bank account number or have your check picked up by courier — before you've had a chance to consider the offer carefully.
- It's not necessary to check out the company with anyone — including your family, lawyer, accountant, local Better Business Bureau or consumer protection agency.
- You don't need written information about the company or its references.
- You can't afford to miss this "high-profit, no-risk" offer.

It's the Law

It also is helpful for people who are the targets of fraudulent telemarketers to know their rights. Anyone who is troubled by calls — whether abusive, deceptive or simply annoying — should know that, under federal law:

- It's illegal for a telemarketer to call you if you have asked not to be called.
- Calling times are restricted to the hours between 8 a.m.

and 9 p.m.

- Telemarketers must tell you it's a sales call, the name of the seller, and what they are selling — before they make their pitch. If it's a prize promotion, they must tell you that you don't have to pay or buy anything to enter or win.
- Telemarketers may not lie about any information, including any facts about their goods or services, the earnings potential, profitability, risk or liquidity of an investment, or the nature of a prize in a prize-promotion scheme.
- Before you pay, telemarketers must tell you the total cost of the goods and any restrictions on getting or using them, or that a sale is final or non-refundable. In a prize promotion, they must tell you the odds of winning, that no purchase or payment is necessary to win and any restrictions or conditions of receiving the prize.
- Telemarketers may not withdraw money from your checking account without your express, verifiable authorization.
- Telemarketers cannot lie to get you to pay.
- You do not have to pay for credit repair, recovery room or advance-fee loan/credit services until these services have been delivered.

How to Protect Targets of Telemarketing Fraud

You also can help people you care about develop responses that will end an unwanted sales call. Possible responses to unwanted callers include: "I don't do business with people I don't know," "Please put me on your 'Do-Not-Call List,'" "I'll need to see written information on your offer before I consider giving you money," or "You can send that information to my attorney's office at . . . ." Perhaps the easiest response is, "I'm not interested. Thank you and good-bye."

Urge your parents or anyone else troubled by calls to resist high-pressure sales tactics. Legitimate businesses respect the

157

fact that a person is not interested. Remind an older person to:

- Say so if they don't want the seller to call back. If they do call back, they're breaking the law. That's a signal to hang up.
- Take their time, and ask for written information about the product, service, investment opportunity or charity that's the subject of the call.
- Talk to a friend, relative or financial advisor before responding to a solicitation. Their financial investments may have consequences for the family or close friends.
- Hang up if they're asked to pay for a prize. Free is free.
- Keep information about their bank accounts and credit cards private unless they know who they're dealing with.
- Hang up if a telemarketer calls before 8 a.m. or after 9 p.m.
- Check out any company with the state and local consumer protection office before they buy any product or service or donate any money as a result of an unsolicited phone call.
- Finally, remind an older person not to send money — cash, check or money order — by courier, overnight delivery or wire to anyone who insists on immediate payment.

If you suspect a scam, call your state attorney general. The Federal Trade Commission's Telemarketing Sales Rule gives state law enforcement officers the power to prosecute fraudulent telemarketers.

For More Information

Consumer Response Center
Federal Trade Commission
Washington, DC 20580
(202) FTC-HELP [382-4357]; TDD: (202) 326-2502
You also can file a complaint with the Commission by contacting the CRC by phone, by mail,by e-mail; use the complaint form at *www.ftc.gov.*

National Consumers League
1701 K Street, NW
Washington, DC 20006
(202) 835-3323
www.natlconsumersleague.org
The National Consumers League and the American Association of Retired Persons conducted research on telemarketing fraud targeting the elderly and offer suggestions for older people and their families in a brochure, *They Can't Hang Up*, available from the National Consumers League.

To *stop telephone sales calls from* many legitimate national marketers, send your name, address and telephone number to:
Direct Marketing Association
Telephone Preference Service
P.O. Box 9014
Farmingdale, NY 11735-9014

To *remove your name* from many national *direct mail lists*, write:
Direct Marketing Association
Mail Preference Service
PO Box 643
Carmel, NY 10512

Prepared by the Federal Trade Commission

Eric's Comments

Consumer Fraud against the elderly is a real concern. This article is targeted to phone fraud but the elderly are prime targets for any type of fraud, or just simply being taken advantage of. We are acutely aware of telemarketers telephoning people using high octane sales pitches that even many younger people can't resist. A telemarketing "land mine" for the elderly, of which we've become aware, is when the elderly place a call to a Credit Card Center, Phone Company, etc., for help. Our experiences teach us that the person answering the telephone is just as much a "selling" telemarketer as those calling outbound although they are cleverly disguised as someone to help us.

We had an elderly client named Ralph who used a cell phone in lieu of a "land line." During our initial contact, we discovered he had a past due cell phone bill for well over $150.00. Part of the balance was for the past thirty days plus his current amount. Ralph's monthly bill was over $75.00. Since he had no significant people to call, either locally or long-distance, our company made a call to get a life line phone. The life line set up should have been less than $10 but before the old guy got off the phone, he had agreed to additional services with a monthly cost exceeding $50. Wow, what a help! We believe Ralph had less than $950 in total income, so this is a big deal; 5.25% of his income going for phone services he didn't need.

Be careful of caregivers as well. I had a friend who balanced checkbooks for elderly clients. She discovered that a caregiver had stolen $100,000 from an elderly gentleman over a period of time. Soon after it was discovered, the gentleman passed away and there was absolutely nothing anyone could do about it. Apparently there was no family and no way to prove anything after his death. Elderly people are grateful for people who care for them and sometimes will give things away that a family member may cherish. In

160

my business, I have my caregivers sign an agreement stating they cannot receive any gifts or items unless they come through our office. This gives us an opportunity to check with family members as to wishes and intent.

Elderly individuals are easy to confuse and easy to take advantage of. You continually hear about "pigeon drop" schemes.

The following information is downloaded from the Missouri Attorney General's web page.

Pigeon Drop Scam
In the pigeon drop scam, swindlers work in pairs or teams. One befriends an unsuspecting consumer, the "pigeon," while the other approaches them with money or valuables he claims to have just found.

After some rehearsed conversation, the con artists agree to split the money three ways with you and arrange to meet at a lawyer's office or somewhere else of their choosing.

But can they trust you, they ask. To get your share, you'll need to put up some "good faith" money, which they will return to you after the goods are divided.

To prove yourself trustworthy, you turn over a large sum of money to them and later go to meet them at the designated spot. Soon after arriving, you realize the pair is long gone -- and so is your money.

Eric's Comments
They can also use bank information schemes, etc., to get your account information and write checks, charges to your accounts, or steal your identity.

The following information is downloaded from the Missouri Attorney General's web page.

Bank Examiner Scheme

In the bank examiner scheme, con artists pose as FBI agents, bank examiners, police officers, detectives or bank officials. These con artists contact you, pretending to need your help to conduct an investigation.

As a valued bank customer or upstanding citizen, you are asked to withdraw your money and hand it over. They promise to redeposit it or return the money to you after they have completed their investigation. Of course, you never see your money again.

Eric's Comments

There are so many schemes and crooks that I can't begin to list them, but you should get the picture. At much younger ages, we still get victimized. So how will it be when we are older? The older we get and the closer to death we perceive ourselves to be, the more vulnerable we are to religious cons as well. We may think that we can buy our way into Heaven. I hear some "preachers" telling us that to get to Heaven, we need to send money to Jesus or God. I respond with a simple question; "Give me Jesus or God's address and I'll send the money directly to Him." I guess these preachers must be some type of go-between since the only address they have is their own.

As we age, we have more difficultly processing multiple pieces of information or formulas, so we may be "ripe for the picking" by unscrupulous individuals. We truly may need someone to watch over us.

21.
Help With Financial Matters

The following information was downloaded for A/PACT.

Aging Parents and Adult Children Together (A/PACT)

DAILY MONEY MANAGEMENT PROGRAMS

(Second in a 10-part series)

You live in a city far from your 75-year-old mother. In telephone conversations during the past year, you've begun to suspect she's growing increasingly forgetful, but she assures you everything is fine. Now a neighbor has called to say your mother hasn't paid her utility bills in three months and the utility company is threatening to cut off the power. What should you do?

If your parent is having trouble managing money, he or she is not alone. An estimated 500,000 older people in the United States need help with their financial affairs. As a result, a new field is evolving to provide daily money management services on a fee-for-service basis.

Daily money managers offer a variety of services:

- Organizing and keeping track of financial and medical insurance records;
- Establishing a budget;
- Helping with check writing and checkbook balancing; and,
- Serving as a representative payee or fiduciary with authority to administer the benefits of people who can't manage their own financial affairs.
- Some money managers also make medical appointments for older clients and help arrange for other assistance, such as locating necessary in-home care. Money managers do not provide financial planning or investment counseling services.

Daily money managers typically charge $25 to $100 an hour, depending on the client's locale and the complexity of their financial affairs. While it is difficult to generalize the total cost, many clients require only a few hours of services each month to keep on top of their finances. Some local governments and community organizations also offer reduced-fee or free services for low-income clients.

Unfortunately, many people do not turn to a daily money manager until after a crisis, such as a threatened eviction or utility cut-off. However, there are ways to tell whether an older person needs a money manager before an emergency occurs. Here's how:

With your parent's help or permission, review his or her checkbook, bank statements and canceled checks. Look for:

- Inappropriate payments, such as payments for medical bills that already have been paid;
- Numerous payments to credit card companies, home

164

shopping networks, sweepstakes or other contests;
- Unusually large donations to charitable or fraternal organizations;
- Failure to list or otherwise track deposits and income;
- Failure to record checks or otherwise track expenditures;
- Lost checkbooks or bank statements;
- Numerous transfers from savings to checking accounts;
- Consistent or unusual payments to a person unknown to you, a possible sign that your parent is being exploited financially.

Then review bills and correspondence, watching for letters from creditors or past-due notices. The review may indicate that a daily money manager is needed.

If you and your parent decide that a daily money manager would be helpful, interview several candidates. Get references and talk with their clients. Also contact the local Better Business Bureau, Chamber of Commerce, local consumer protection agency or area agency on aging. Ask if they have any unresolved consumer complaints on file. One caveat: No record of complaints against a particular provider doesn't necessarily mean no previous consumer problems. It may be that problems exist, but have not yet been reported, or that the money manger is doing business under several different names. In addition, ask the providers you interview for their company's financial statement to make sure the provider you choose has a solid financial history. Make sure the provider is familiar with the special needs of older people.

For More Information

The Eldercare Locator — a nationwide, toll-free assistance directory sponsored by the National Association of Area Agencies on Aging — will refer you to the area agency on aging nearest to your parent or other older adult. (800) 677-

1116, *www.aoa.dhhs.gov/elderpage/locator.html.*
American Association of Daily Money Managers
P.O. Box 755
Silver Spring, MD 20918
(301) 593-5462
www.aadmm.com/listof.htm
The association can provide names of daily money managers in an older person's community or nearby. The association also publishes *Daily Money Management: What It Is and How Can It Help Me?*

Federal Deposit Insurance Corp.
801 17th Street, NW
Washington, DC 20434-0001
(800) 276-6003 or (202) 416-6940
fax: (202) 416-2076
e-mail: publicinfo@fdic.gov
www.fdic.gov/consumer/consnews/sum97
The FDIC publishes Financial Caregiving: A Survival Guide.

Prepared by the American Association of Retired Persons

Eric's Comments

Daily Money Management Programs: This article seems pretty basic. I'm so concerned with people taking advantage of the elderly that I'd be really careful. Our company believes in having a Care Manager to watch over an elderly loved one who does not live close to you. The elderly typically don't respond well when they are faced with too many choices or too many people to deal with. They want things simple and well-defined, without a lot of commotion or turmoil built in. If it is a matter of day-to-day care, managing their checkbook, paying bills, being fed nutritionally, etc., then a Care Manager can coordinate these activities. A Care Manager can even evaluate other living arrangements or inspect current living spaces for safety, etc. They manage the day to day living assistance for an elderly client who has no one else close by. If the need is financial advice, investment or legal advice, etc., then the Care Manager can make arrangements for appropriate advisors based on their knowledge of area resources.

22.
Alzheimer's

I have downloaded the following reference material.

The Seven Warning Signs of Alzheimer's Disease

The purpose of this list is to alert the public to the early warning signs of one of the most devastating disorders affecting older people — Alzheimer's disease. If someone has several or even most of these symptoms, it does not mean they definitely have the disease. It does mean they should be thoroughly examined by a medical specialist trained in evaluating memory disorders, such as a neurologist or a psychiatrist, or by a comprehensive memory disorder clinic, with an entire team of expert knowledge about memory problems.

The seven warning signs of Alzheimer's disease are:

1. Asking the same question over and over again.
2. Repeating the same story, word for word, again and again.
3. Forgetting how to cook, or how to make repairs, or how to play cards — activities that were previously done with ease and regularity.
4. Losing one's ability to pay bills or balance one's checkbook.
5. Getting lost in familiar surroundings, or misplacing household objects.
6. Neglecting to bathe, or wearing the same clothes over

and over again, while insisting that they have taken a bath or that their clothes are still clean.

7. Relying on someone else, such as a spouse, to make decisions or answer questions they previously would have handled themselves.

Reprinted with the permission of The Suncoast Gerontology Center, University of South Florida. Revised 9/01/99.
Page last updated Mar 02, 2006

Definition of Alzheimer's

- Alzheimer's disease is a progressive, degenerative disorder that attacks the brain's nerve cells, or neurons, resulting in loss of memory, thinking and language skills, and behavioral changes.

- These neurons, which produce the brain chemical, or neurotransmitter, acetylcholine, break connections with other nerve cells and ultimately die. For example, short-term memory fails when Alzheimer's disease first destroys nerve cells in the hippocampus, and language skills and judgment decline when neurons die in the cerebral cortex.

- Two types of abnormal lesions clog the brains of individuals with Alzheimer's disease: Beta-amyloid plaques— sticky clumps of protein fragments and cellular material that form outside and around neurons; and neurofibrillary tangles—insoluble twisted fibers composed largely of the protein tau that build up inside nerve cells. Although these structures are hallmarks of the disease, scientists are unclear whether they cause it or a byproduct of it.

- Alzheimer's disease is the most common cause of dementia, or loss of intellectual function, among people aged 65 and older.

- Alzheimer's disease is not a normal part of aging.

- Origin of the term Alzheimer's disease dates back to 1906 when Dr. Alois Alzheimer, a German physician,

170

presented a case history before a medical meeting of a 51-year-old woman who suffered from a rare brain disorder. A brain autopsy identified the plaques and tangles that today characterize Alzheimer's disease.

Alzheimer's Foundation of America 866.AFA.8484 http://www. alzfdn.org/

Definition of Dementia

- Dementia is a general term that describes a group of symptoms-such as loss of memory, judgment, language, complex motor skills, and other intellectual function-caused by the permanent damage or death of the brain's nerve cells, or neurons.
- One or more of several diseases, including Alzheimer's disease, can cause dementia.
- Alzheimer's disease is the most common cause of dementia in persons over the age of 65. It represents about 60 percent of all dementias.
- The other most common causes of dementia are vascular dementia, caused by stroke or blockage of blood supply, and dementia with Lewy bodies. Other types include alcohol dementia, caused by sustained use of alcohol; trauma dementia, caused by head injury; and a rare form of dementia, frontotemporal dementia.
- The clinical symptoms and the progression of dementia vary, depending on the type of disease causing it, and the location and number of damaged brain cells. Some types progress slowly over years, while others may result in sudden loss of intellectual function.
- Each type of dementia is characterized by different pathologic, or structural, changes in the brain, such as an accumulation of abnormal plaques and tangles in individuals with Alzheimer's disease, and abnormal tau protein in individuals with frontotemporal dementia.

Alzheimer's Foundation of America 866.AFA.8484 http://www.alzfdn.org/

12 Ways to Boost Caregiver Success

1. Educate yourself about the disease. Read books, attend workshops and consult with healthcare professionals.
2. Learn caregiving techniques. Key areas are communication skills, safety concerns, and managing behavioral challenges and activities of daily living.
3. Understand the experience of your loved one. Adjust your expectations. Be patient and kind.
4. Avoid caregiver burnout. Make time for yourself. Join caregiver support groups. Pursue interests beyond your caregiving role, such as exercise, hobbies, journaling and art.
5. Maintain your own physical and mental health. Exercise, respite and other activities can reduce stress. Seek medical help if there are signs of depression.
6. Discuss the situation with family and friends. Support systems are critical.
7. Do cognitive stimulation activities with your loved one. Listening to music, word puzzles and memory games can easily be done at home.
8. Foster communication with physicians. Be involved in your loved one's medical care. Ask questions about the progression of the disease, express concerns and discuss treatment options.
9. Take care of financial, legal and long-term care planning issues. Try to involve your loved one in decision-making, if they are still capable of providing input, and consider their wishes related to future care and end-of-life issues.
10. Smile. Kindness, humor and creativity are essential parts of caregiving. Hugs, hand massage and other gentle physical contact will help your loved one feel connected and loved.
11. Think positive. Focus on your loved one's remaining strengths and enjoy your relationship while you are still able to.

12. Reach out for care. Call the Alzheimer's Foundation of America—866.AFA.8484, for counseling, information and referrals to local resources nationwide.

Alzheimer's Foundation of America 866.AFA.8484 http://www.alzfdn.org/

Planning

Families who have a loved one with dementia should take a look at legal and financial issues—the sooner, the better. Advance planning may enable individuals with dementia to provide input into the decision-making before loss of cognitive abilities prevents them from doing so. In addition, advance planning may relieve some of the burden on caregivers and other family members when important issues arise during the progression of the disease.

Here are some issues to consider:

- Review of financial resources and investment portfolios, including bank and investment accounts, bonds, Social Security, and employer pensions.
- Insurance coverage, including health, disability, life, prescription drug, and long-term care.
- Long-term care options, including in-home care, assisted living facilities and nursing homes.
- End-of-life wishes regarding life-sustaining procedures such as cardiopulmonary resuscitation (CPR), artificial feeding and artificial breathing, and palliative care (treatments to manage symptoms and relieve pain).
- Preparation of estate planning documents and advance directives, such as a will, a living will that states end-of-life wishes and a durable power of attorney that appoints a person to make medical decisions on an individual's behalf.
- Hospice care—and whether this care for the terminally ill should be provided at home or in a hospital or long-

term care facility.

Alzheimer's Foundation of America 866.AFA.8484 http://www.alzfdn.org/

Eric's Comments

There are people who specialize in Alzheimer's who are very knowledgeable. It is important to consult with those who work with Alzheimer's patients on a regular basis. At the least, it is complex with very few answers. In my opinion, we are moving into a society that diagnoses any type of memory failure or strange behavior as Alzheimer's. Since Alzheimer's can only be truly identified by autopsy, families may never know for sure. An excerpt from an article taken from "Health A to Z" website that was reviewed by David N. Neubauer, MD, Assistant Professor of Psychiatry, The Johns Hopkins University School of Medicine in Baltimore, Md. states:

> *"Diagnosing Alzheimer's can be a frustrating experience for both the patient and the physician. That's because no simple test exists for diagnosing Alzheimer's. There's no way to see the telltale tangles and plaques in the brain while the patient is still alive."*

The article indicates there are diagnostic tools available today that are reliable. It states:

> *"Studies show that doctors are correct in diagnosing Alzheimer's about 90 percent of the time."*

I've learned from reading that dementia is a form of Alzheimer's, so I'm speaking of it as well. These are very real issues and should not be take lightly. The more you can read about and understand Alzheimer's issues, the better you will be equipped to handle it. There are things that can help the patient and family cope with this disease. I'll share a few things from my limited experiences.

We were contracted to care for a husband and wife (Charles and Gertrude) in their nineties who had just returned from a trip to their son's home in the East. They'd been married for over sixty-five years and lived in their same home for a number of years. Gertrude had Alzheimer's and, as we began care, the family indicated the symptoms were confusion and wandering away. There was family pressure to move them from their home but they didn't want to move. There was discussion about moving only the wife. The husband said he had taken an oath to care for her, and he wasn't going to leave her nor let her go. During the siblings' discussions, the couple visited their son in the East. He was going to see how they were doing and make a recommendation. Gertrude encountered numerous health problems during the visit and the Alzheimer's worsened. By the time they arrived home, she was in bad shape.

The local sibling (Paula) wanted, with our help, to try to keep them in their home. We placed two twenty-four hour companion caregivers to work with this couple. One worked three twenty-four hour shifts, and the other worked four shifts. The husband, Charles, had been providing the bulk of the care with the help of Paula. By this time Charles could no longer provide adequate care for Gertrude.

As we first took over the case, Gertrude's situation was critical. She required a hospitalization for a gastric illness plus had many eating and sleeping problems. As the companions settled in and the couple settled into their new routine, Gertrude improved. The routine of very low or no stimulation, staying within her known surroundings, and proper rest and diet were helping. After about thirty days, the situation was vastly improved. They were able to stay in their own home until the husband's health failed. This experience taught me that being in her own surroundings with proper nutrition and rest, plus having a predictable low stress

175

environment allowed Gertrude to do much better.

 We have, on staff, a Care Coordinator for those whose adult children either live out of town or are over-whelmed by their own commitments. The Care Coordinator can assist with family meetings to enable the family to create and implement a plan of care for their loved one.

23.
Spirituality:
Listening To God's Word

We received the following e-mail (this is as received, not edited):

"Have you ever received a phone call one day out of the blue that turns your life into a different direction and you don't have the knowledge even for that direction? This is what happen to me. My name is Tilley and I live in Arkansas and after 30 years I received a phone call from my cousin Hubert who lives in Springfield, Missouri. Hubert needed a new place to live as he had lived with his girlfriend and her father for all these years but now the father had passed away.

This may not seem like a problem to most but my cousin Hubert is not only 70 years old with huge health problems (diabetic, insult depended who must give himself injections and keep track of his blood sugar, medications and a heart pacemaker) but he is also retarded. He also is illiterate and has very limited concepts of paying his bills or what money even is.

First things first was to find him a small apartment. Between the paper work and the waiting list this was done in a 3 month time frame. But Hubert needed someone to check in on him and to help him as a caretaker and I knew this but where or how was the next question. Next was to open the phone book and just start calling until someone out there helped Hubert and I.

Southwest Missouri Aging returned my phone call and put me on a waiting list. As I hung up the phone I thought okay at least there is a list out there but how long a year or two? At this time I was driving up and back from Missouri to Arkansas twice a week and my gas budget was not only gone but this was to much for anyone to keep pace with. You may ask me why I just didn't move him to Arkansas with me. How could I when his whole life had been in Springfield, Mo. And he had a life there. Hubert goes to church on Sundays and Wednesdays, he goes bowling on Mondays, he takes classes on Thursday, he has a brother in the nursing home that he goes and sees, he has a girlfriend whom he loves. I had already upset his world with moving him away from all he had known for 30 years and put him on his own in a strange apartment with all kinds of neighbor that he did not know. Keep in mind Hubert is retarded and life had given him a new direction too and he did not like it either.

They called me back and told me that they could provide me a caretaker now. You will never understand or even realize how wonderful those words were to me. If there was a way you could hug someone through the phone he received that hug from me. Hubert now had not only a caretaker he had made a new friend named Sue. How do I even type into words what a lady named Sue does for Hubert and for I. Oh yes she makes his apartment shine. But cleaning his apartment is just a small part of what Sue does. She washes his clothes, she cooks his meals, she checks to make sure he takes his medications; she makes his shopping list, all the things a caretaker is to do. But there is another list that know one maybe aware of as it isn't charted or recorded. As I stated Hubert is or I should say was illiterate but he is taking classes to learn to read at 70 years old now. Sue makes him write his shopping list as he says he needs bread and Sue tells him to write it on the list. He tells her he can't and she tells him to take the bread wrapper and write it as he can do it. Just one small thing to most but Hubert is so proud as he

178

hands me the list with his word bread that Sue had showed him how to write. Sue is helping him to read and write for the first time in Hubert's life. She brings him books and explains where he can go to the book-mobile and get his own books too. The wonderful world of books is coming to a retarded man of 70 years old now because of a lady named Sue.

Sue on her own time has gone to the store for Hubert also. He has had to have special things that are sugar free. Sue goes to the store for him after work and stops them back by his apartment for him. This is beyond her duties and it is rare to find this kind of caring today.

Hubert looks forward to her arrival every Monday and Thursday. If he ever needs her she is there for him. His words: I love MY Sue! I think this says it all.

As for me thank you is not the right words but they are the only ones I have. My life is my life now and it is all because of this program. If I had to move Hubert again I have know idea what that would do to him. My guess is he would retreat into himself and die. Does it sound to dramatic to say that this program may save Hubert's life? Maybe not?"

The program Tilley refers to is administered through the Southwest Missouri Office on Aging and is funded by the Greene County Senior Citizens Tax Fund. Services are provided by local providers and Sue is an employee of Assisting Aging Parents. I include this *unedited* writing to illustrate the positive impact in-home care provides for families. Hubert is in his own home, and his cousin has her own life. She obviously cares for Hubert and will do what it takes to see he is cared for; however, this allows both of them to maintain their independence.

I've been through a lot and continue to face health and financial problems each day. The one thing that I know for sure is that there is a God. I am very spiritual and believe that one of the best prayers I've heard is, "I pray not for God

179

to be on our side, but for us to be on God's side."

I don't believe that God directs or dabbles in our every move or our everyday activities. I believe we should be full of God's spirit, peace, and love and then be able to "do the right thing," without having to think about it. It should become a part of "who we are."

It is my belief that some organized religions, bureaucrats, and leaders of foreign nations, who seem dedicated to taking us back two thousand years, are focusing on "control of our thoughts." Religion can be vastly over thought. The Golden Rule, "Do unto others as you would have them do unto you," should be easy if we practice it. We are only responsible for our actions, not the actions of others. As we provide services for the elderly, this seems to be the one primary Biblical passage that applies. "Honor thy Father and Mother" is another yet it doesn't reflect any clear course of action. Jesus died when he was a young man; therefore, aging issues weren't applicable. As we deal with aging issues and caring for the elderly, we better remember that what we do may be the way we are treated when we get older. The practices and structures we create now may one day be utilized for us. I believe God created a wonderful world and intended unlimited possibilities for all mankind. It is too bad that some members of mankind get in the way of others. We continually make choices, some of them good, some bad. I believe that the peace of God (call him Christ, Buddha, or anything else) is available for us both when times are good and times are bad. I believe there are always answers out there. We need to be wise enough to find them. When we think about how we will spend our eternity, it seems to me it is about the legacy we leave. For us, what remains on earth after we are gone is the memory of our life. Not who we are, but who we were; the impact we've had on others. The movie, "It's a Wonderful Life" does a good job of depicting the impact of an ordinary man on other people's lives. It begs the question, "If you hadn't been born, how would other lives be changed?"

I'm writing this chapter at Christmas time which, for most of us, brings up a lot of memories, both good and bad. It also highlights the fact that our actions of today are the memories of tomorrow. We are in control of how we are remembered. We are in control of how we handle each day. I keep for my personal focus two writings. The first is from Charles Swindoll, an evangelical Christian pastor, titled "Attitude":

"The longer I live, the more I realize the impact of attitude on life. Attitude, to me, is more important than facts. It is more important than the past; than education, than money, than circumstances, than failures, than success, than what other people think or say or do. It is more important than appearance, giftedness, or skill. It will make or break a company...a church...a home. The remarkable thing is we have a choice everyday regarding the attitude we will embrace for that day. We cannot change our past...we cannot change the fact that people will act in a certain way. We cannot change the inevitable. The only thing we can do is play on the one thing we have, and that is our attitude... I am convinced that life is 10% what happens to me and 90% how I react to it. And so it is with you...we are in charge of our Attitudes."

The other is from an unknown author:

"This is the beginning of a New Day. God has given me this day to use as I will. I can waste it or grow in its light and be of service to others. But what I do with this day is important because I have exchanged a day of my life for it. When tomorrow comes, today will be gone forever. I hope I will not regret the price I paid for it."

We have, are, or will be dealing with aging parents or loved ones. It is a challenge. We must "make friends with it" and accept "this" is the situation we are in, whether we like it or not. We can go "kicking and screaming" or learn what we can, and to the best of our imperfect human abilities, live in a manner that honors us and our elder loved ones. "What would Jesus do?" Some days we will kick and scream anyway. We are imperfect mortals after all. This seems to be the way God created us. Everyone has a bad day or more. Be gentle with yourself (as Jesus would have you to be). Get up and try to do better tomorrow. How can you help someone else if you don't take care of yourself or are busy beating yourself up?

In many cases, there are actions by the elderly over which we are powerless. Turn those actions over to your Higher Power and concentrate on the things that you can control. The Serenity Prayer states, "God grant me the serenity to accept the things I cannot change, the power to change the things I can, and the wisdom to know the difference."

You are trading a day of your life for today, what are you going to do with it? The choices you make today impact the quality of tomorrow. Aging is inevitable, dying a certainty. Life is a journey, and we need to make it the best it can be. We will face the decisions we make toward our aging parents or loved ones both at their funerals and again as we are cared for in our own aging process. For my peace of mind, I try to follow the "Golden Rule" and I recommend it to you as well.

Twelve Step Comparison

As I speak on the subject of aging and issues dealing with the elderly, I repeatedly think that the twelve step Alcoholics Anonymous program applies to this as well. The following step outline is my take on AA's program as it applies to dealing with aging parents, relatives, or friends. You may be the care provider or not.

Step 1: We admitted we were (substitute are) powerless over alcohol (substitute the actions of elderly loved one) and that our lives have become unmanageable. I've already written that as we age we develop habits and mannerisms. The thought that you are going to have much impact on the behavior of someone ninety years old is absurd. You may be able to tweak their behavior or slightly alter it, but at ninety we are who we are. If they have dementia or Alzheimer's, it also isn't somehow miraculously going to be changed. They are who they are. Like it or not, the situation is what it is. Kicking and screaming isn't going to change it; kicking and screaming only gets in the way of positive, realistic action we are able to take.

Step 2: Came to believe that a Power greater than ourselves could restore us to sanity. We are often in an "insane" situation, and insane situations can cause insane behavior. Just as pouring out alcohol is no solution for alcoholism (because they can buy more tomorrow), yelling at someone with Alzheimer's is not going to make them have less dementia. I am a very spiritual Christian, not evangelical, just a believer. If you've been where I've been and had to handle what I've handled, then you would have no doubt about a Higher Power. God's answer to prayer isn't always what we want to hear. I believe that typically God only intervenes when we allow Him to because we can no longer carry the burden alone and are open to help. God can guide us about the best way to handle difficult situations.

Step 3: Made a decision to turn our will and our lives over to the care of God as we understood Him. I lost a wife of thirty-four years, my Mother died five weeks later, and then Dad died two years after that. I've faced financial ruin. I've had my life threatened. I almost died at age thirteen from a childhood illness. In the past two years, I've been hospitalized ten times, had eleven or twelve surgeries and three major infections. I also have had a wonderful life.

I have beautiful, successful children and wonderful grand-children. My children are also my friends. I have a new wife who is a gift from God. We live in a home in a beautiful, safe part of the country with green rolling hills, flowers, and many nearby lakes. We have a cat, a dog, a guinea named Gus, and a herd of deer living in our woods. Our Labrador, Carson, eagerly fetches the paper each morning unless terrified by a thunder storm. I have wonderful man toys, including a spare pickup truck, boat, tractor, barn, tools... everything a guy could ask. We attend a wonderful church, have good friends, take vacations regularly to the beach, and get by financially each month. I am a very happy person. My personal prayer is, "God, please fill me with your peace and spirit and grant me the wisdom to feel it." There is a popular bracelet that asks the question "What would Jesus do?" My prayer asks for me to have the "spirit" so I can act, as Jesus or whatever you call your God would act, without having to think about it. If you are full of his Spirit and follow His guidance, your actions will be as His! My wife adds, "God's will is for the greater good of all concerned." How can you go wrong with that? It is through our toughest times that we turn to God and grow.

Step 4: Made a searching and fearless moral inventory of ourselves. As we make this journey with our elderly, we often try to understand, "Why is life like this?" I believe that we must make our decisions based on how we are going to feel when we see them at the funeral. This means we are responsible for how we act, no matter how they've treated us. This may be a time to look at your own personal issues and consider working on them. Especially be aware of our need to control. Often being in control is a way to feel safe. Being organized is an asset. But continually trying to get others to do it "our way," regardless of their feelings, can be a problem. It can create stress for us and everyone around us. Admittedly, working on ourselves is often very difficult and painful. It often requires the help of a counselor, pastor, trusted friend, family member, or a self-help group such as Al-Anon. This is hard work. It takes a lot of time, but the results can turn your life in a positive direction you once thought impossible. My wife is proof positive of this. She figured out that instead of being depressed, she had been through fifteen bad years. For her, those years ended sixteen years ago. Ultimately, the end of *our* lives is about us. The end of the lives of our elderly is about *them*. It will be our turn soon enough. Try not to let your issues about yesterday affect your decisions of today. This is certainly easier said than done. Some days we probably won't make it. But we can process our feelings in whatever way works for us; then get up tomorrow, be gentle with ourselves, and try again. You may need to compartmentalize different parts of your life during this time. Take things one day at a time.

Step 5: Admitted to God, to ourselves, and to another human being the exact nature of our wrongs. Regardless how difficult it is, we can still consider what we have to face at the funeral. As long as they have life, you have an opportunity to set things right. (That is unless your struggle is with undeserved guilt even though you have done everything humanly possible.) You can make amends or ask questions about their situations in life and earlier actions toward you. It may be they had struggles of which you were totally unaware. I wrote earlier about "baggage." You can pack additional bags or you can leave some of the heavy load at the funeral. It's your choice.

Step 6: Were entirely ready to have God remove all these defects of character. Never will we humans have all our defects of character removed! Remember, no human being is perfect. We all have our strengths and vulnerabilities. Be sure to give yourself credit for your strengths. Believe me, never asking for help is not a strength. If you don't believe you have any strengths, please seek counseling. Pick a couple of your vulnerabilities and write about how they show up in this particular situation. You can focus on taking baby steps that will lead you in a better direction. For example, if you are totally burned out, take the step of asking someone for help in one small area. Ask a sibling to do one load of laundry a week. If they refuse and you're doing everything, it sure gives you clarity about the situation. At least, do one thing that is kind for you. But, God will help when, and if, we become honest, open, and willing. An AA slogan applies, "Progress, not perfection." Just pray, follow God's guidance to the best of your ability, and take at least small steps toward living as our loving God would have us live. It is important to allow yourself the knowledge that humans will never do everything exactly right. And you are human, right?

One of the most powerful lessons I've learned is to "forgive myself." Sometimes you are just peddling as fast as you can. You can only give 100%, that's all you've got to give. Pray for wisdom and peace.

Step 7: Humbly asked Him to remove our shortcomings. If you are having trouble with decisions you've made that you regret, don't tune out God, ask for peace and understanding from Him.

Step 8: Made a list of all persons we had harmed, and became willing to make amends to them all. In the case of elder care, it is a good idea to be sure that you tie up any loose emotional ends with your elders. Don't neglect to express appreciation and say, "I love you," "I'm sorry," "I forgive you," when appropriate or "I understand." This may apply to you or to your elderly loved ones with unresolved issues. It is unbelievable the healing that can move from some simple communication. I encourage you to do it before it is too late. It is never too late to say or hear, "I'm sorry."

Step 9: Made direct amends to such people wherever possible, except when to do so would injure them or others. My deceased wife Judy had been a primary caregiver for Mom and Dad until her death. She had been raised in a

186

more "touchy-feely" environment than my family. It was normal for her to hug and kiss my parents. Mom and Dad were very responsive, and I believe at the end-of-life it was very comforting to them. My sister was there one night as this was happening and commented, "Why don't Mom and Dad do that with me?" Of course, she had not been raised this way and it was awkward for her. My words for my sister were, "As long as they are alive and aware, there is still opportunity to hug and kiss them and tell them you love them." In some relationships, this may not be possible due to issues about how you were treated when you were a child. Be willing to listen to their amends, even when they are unable to put them in the words you would like to hear.

A woman in her forties with unresolved issues with her parents was terminally ill with cancer. Joyce had worked hard on her emotional issues and had become a wise, spiritual individual. Near her end, she wisely said, "The only time left is for love." Maybe we should use another AA slogan, "How important is it?" Maybe it is very important. But perhaps, in the grand scheme of things, it isn't really important. Perhaps it's time to let go.

How you handle the end may be yours to consider for the rest of your life. "To pack or unpack" baggage, that is the question!

Step 10: Continued to take personal inventory and when we were wrong promptly admitted it. Sometimes our emotions run away with us. We become overwhelmed with the issues or ups and downs of our situation. It is important to continually focus on the task at hand. As I made this journey with my parents, I had to emotionally detach from them to a certain degree. I had to continually remind myself that it was their end, not mine. They weren't going to get any younger, brighter, or more functional. As they say, "It's all downhill from here." It is normal to sometimes lose your patience with them. When you do, make amends, and continue to do the best you can.

Step 11: Sought through prayer and meditation to improve our conscious contact with God as we understood Him, praying only for knowledge of His will for us and the power to carry that out. My prayer is as always, "Fill me with your spirit, peace, and love and give me the strength to face whatever is to come." You continually hear that God will not give you more than you can handle. One of the methods to handle enormous problems is to release to God the things you can't do anything about. Ask him to show you the next right step to take. The serenity prayer is appropriate for dealing with these issues. The complete Serenity Prayer:

God, give us grace to accept with serenity
the things that cannot be changed,
Courage to change the things
which should be changed,
and the Wisdom to distinguish
the one from the other.

Living one day at a time,
Enjoying one Moment at a time,
Accepting hardship as a pathway to peace,
Taking, as Jesus did,
This sinful world as it is,
Not as I would have it,
Trusting that You will make all things right,
If I surrender to Your will,
So that I may be reasonably happy in this life,
And supremely happy with You forever in the next.
Amen.

by Reinhold Niebuhr (1892-1971)Complete,
Unabridged, Original Version.

The most common form of this prayer stops after:

God, give us grace to accept with serenity
the things that cannot be changed,
Courage to change the things
which should be changed,
and the Wisdom to distinguish
the one from the other.

This prayer is extremely applicable when dealing with our aging parents. Take it to heart, you will use it frequently.

Step 12: Having had a spiritual awakening as the result of these steps, we tried to carry this message to alcoholics, and to practice these principles in all our affairs. Instead of alcoholics, substitute "the people now dealing with aging issues." We can share our stories with others dealing with similar problems and those who are yet to face this crisis. There are multiple right answers and methods for this journey. People's situations will vary greatly. I'm writing from my perspective hoping to be helpful to those headed into this journey. I know if you haven't faced this issue, you will. In the future, support group activities will increase. We attend trade shows and seminars and discuss these issues with many people. It seems people who have completed the journey are willing to share their feelings. I encourage the sharing. Get as much information as you can and adapt it to your journey.

There are additional applicable terms used at twelve step meetings. Enablers, co-dependents, and denial are the most common which "cross over" and can be applied to issues of aging. Denial is the most common and is applicable to those aging as well as those who ultimately will be responsible for their care. None of us want to admit we are getting older. We don't want to lose our independence nor become a burden on anybody. Most of us seem to think we've somehow found the Fountain of Youth. I said many times that, if I didn't own a mirror, I'd think I was twenty-five, not sixty-two. The harsh reality is, I own the mirror. We need to be the best we can be for the age we are. We can't turn back the clock. I'm not suggesting that we give up or get the idea we've suddenly become worthless; quite the contrary. Our lives are changing. Activities that we were able to do when we were younger may now be dangerous. I wrote earlier about an incident where my wife and I were "skinny dipping" and couldn't get back into the boat. My recommendation was not to stop the activity, just park the boat on the bank and wade into the water.

I have circulation problems in both my legs and can't walk very far. In the past, we could go anywhere, park anywhere, and walk anywhere. Now I park closer to the door and save as many strides as possible. I haven't stopped going, I just take elevators in lieu of stairs and do a better job of planning my route. We changed our season basketball tickets to our local university for seats that have access to handrails. We were on the fifteenth bleacher row until my sixty year old wife fell on her bottom. That was a signal for change. I am suggesting we be as active as possible; just recognize how we've changed. Driving will become another peril. Already my eyes don't adjust to night driving as well as they used to.

Denial, however, is also widely practiced by adult children when evaluating their parents. It isn't natural for our children to see us as vulnerable. If they realize we are failing, it will have an impact on their lives as well as ours. It can be painful for them to recognize. We don't want to become dependent or a burden on them. They don't want us to be either because they have problems of their own. The most romantic idea is that we are doing great and will live forever. You hear the kids say, "I visited my ninety year old Dad, and he's doing as well as he ever did." Of course; this isn't possible, but if our observation is different it creates demands on both parties. We assume some responsibilities for Dad, and he has to give up some independence. Neither side wants this to happen, so we deny the problem.

We become enablers by not facing reality. When we see our parents, we see the future for us. None of us want to face our own mortality. Most of us don't take any action until there is a crisis. If you think about it, it would be easier to make small adjustments as we age so that it is as seamless as possible. We don't want to be a burden but we don't do anything to keep this from happening. Denial of our situation generally results in creating the very thing we are trying not to have happen. If we don't make our home safer or get some small incremental help at some point, we might have a major breakdown. In the long run, it is much easier on all parties concerned to realize and assess our situation and continually make it as good as it can be for the age we are.

24.

Will Our Grandchildren Know Who We Were?

Preserving Life Stories and Family Histories

By Ann Naegler, MA, LCSW

From the time I was a young child, mother told me stories about her family's history. They were quite illustrious folks. As I grew older and the relationship with mother deteriorated, I "tuned out" just about everything she said. We get tired of hearing the same stories over and over again. I felt that, in comparison with "her illustrious family," I was pretty much a nothing. It's too bad that I never got to know some nice family members because I felt so inferior to them. Mom judged people by how much money and power they had, who their ancestors were and, if you were female, how good you looked and how successful your husband was. Of course, you had to go to the right schools and belong to the right fraternities and sororities. Naturally, you were married and had two beautiful, perfect children. Because I never lived up to any of that, I didn't want to hear about it. I subsequently went on a life-long search to figure out why I was the way I was and why my parents were the way they were.

I had some time in 2000 and *wanted* to learn some more about my family history. I knew there was Native American (Cherokee) in my ancestry. I believe the story stated that my great grandmother was on the Cherokee Trail of Tears. Grandmother Irene was a beautiful woman with long blue-black hair and black eyes. Hence, her nickname was Blackie. All the women in the family of that era had black hair and eyes. I have olive skin and almond shaped eyes, like my favorite Aunt Billie. I asked the eldest family member Great Aunt Florence about this. She was 92, very sharp, and was just back from seeing Broadway plays. When I asked her, she became quite indignant and haughtily stated, "There's no Native American in OUR family! Whatever are you talking about?" I was quite confused by her reaction because I knew she was in the same family as Grandmother Irene, and there was most certainly Native American in Grandmother's history. There I figured it out. In Aunt Florence's day, it wasn't cool to be Native American; hence her denial. How much do we not know about our background because of denial? Is this fair? Don't we have the right to know about our backgrounds? After all, they influence who we are. Most of us want to understand ourselves better, as well as our families.

Then my quest became even more personal. I truly know my father was a wonderful man, but something had never been quite right. That something was alcoholism. I was born when both of my parents were over 40. As I grew up, I guess my father's alcoholism was advanced, even though he was able to operate a small business. His liver quit when he was fifty-seven and I was fifteen. It turned out he was the most emotionally stable family member. When he died, mom's alcoholism took off. Both had the disease of alcoholism and they couldn't control their drinking. Recognizing this is a step toward forgiveness.

I looked for answers about what my parents had been like when they were young adults before alcoholism had taken such a toll. I asked various people about them and don't feel my questions were ever really answered. As in the case of my Native American ancestry, anyone who had the answers was either gone or could no longer tell me.

How I regret not writing down mom's stories! How many of us feel that way? It may not be too late for you to do this. I encourage you to do this because I can almost guarantee that this is going to mean a lot to someone someday.

I had been a Social Worker for twenty-eight years and my career was beginning to wind down. Now what was I going to do for the rest of my life? We have many wonderful opportunities to reinvent ourselves, and this was such a time for me.

I had done Adoptive and Foster Home Studies for twenty years. A number of people I worked with commented on how much self-knowledge and understanding they gained from answering my questions and considering their lives; even if their goal hadn't been to parent children. The knowledge had been a bonus.

A number of similar questions are asked in completing a Social History. I got the idea that the material could be modified to ask others in completing a review of their lives and preserving their family histories. Of course, I later learned that I wasn't the only one to come up with this idea.

I first worked with my ninety-two-year-old father-in-law, James, who seemed to thoroughly enjoy talking about his life. (This has been true in every single instance. There is both laughter and tears. People do not have to discuss anything they wish to keep private.) James especially enjoyed talking about his sweetheart, Charlotte, who had passed on a year earlier after over sixty-eight years of marriage. They met at a party in 1938 where they danced, played croquet, pulled taffy, and ate homemade ice cream. He admitted that Charlotte had a very lovely shape. On their third date James said, "If you'll marry me, I'll make a million dollars." She accepted but had to loan him three dollars when they married thirty days later. Their favorite song was "Stardust."

James was a bright, complicated man. When he was a young child, his family was affluent. In 1922 when he was nine, his father died suddenly during an influenza epidemic.

195

The young widow was unable to cope with telling her three young sons; thus, she didn't. The little boys waited by the gate every day for three weeks watching for their beloved father to return before they finally learned he was not coming home. This left a life-long sensitivity to loss.

The family's financial resources were eventually gone and they became poor. James recalls doing anything to make a dime and having holes in his shoes covered with cardboard. This had a profound effect on his life. He graduated from high school in 1929 at the beginning of the Great Depression. He worked all the time and finally made the million dollars he promised his young bride.

James worked seven days a week while his four children were growing up and consequently he missed ball games and dance recitals. His children may have doubted his love many times and saw him to be a hard man. However, the greatest love James could give was through providing for his family; doing what hadn't been done for him as a child. The only way to feel safe was to have money. Not having money meant not being safe. No wonder he worked all the time! James talked about his four successful children and his pride in them. He may have never told them this. In fact, when he passed away a year later and his Legacy Life Story was read at the service, his children learned things about him they hadn't known and were able to see him in a different light. What a gift!

Next, a friend asked me to write her father's life story. It was an amazing one. Frank lived in an orphanage as a child and sold newspapers on a street corner. He too graduated from high school in 1929. When he couldn't find work, he joined the Navy. He fell while on ship and seriously injured his back. He had multiple back surgeries and was declared disabled.

He didn't like being unproductive so he began to read, beginning with the Dictionary. He received a Navy pension of thirteen dollars per month, spent thirteen dollars on a piano, and took lessons from an elderly neighbor. Since he couldn't work, he seriously studied the piano and, in the opinions of many, could have become a concert pianist. After another surgery, he was able to return to work. He worked for an electric company and literally turned on lights across rural Missouri. He married and raised two productive children. Frank was at the end of his life when I interviewed him and he felt he hadn't accomplished much during his lifetime.

After I finished writing his story, he called with new information. He said there was something his son thought should be added, although Frank himself thought it was "nothing." What was the "nothing?" As a youth, he saved a young man from drowning. While in the Navy, he saved another man from drowning. These are two lives he saved, plus all these gentlemen went on to contribute during their lifetimes – including the contributions of their children and grandchildren. I can only hope that this helped Frank realize how much his life mattered. How many of us feel we haven't done much with our lives? We need to look at what we have contributed; probably far more than we think.

Thus, my business, Legacies Life Stories, in Springfield, Missouri, was born. I can't tell you how many times people have said, "I would give anything to have this information about my mom or dad or family. I wish I had listened and written things down." How many of us feel this way? Well, it isn't too late. Most of the Legacies I have recently done have been about people who are already gone. It isn't too late when we still have the memories in our hearts.

I include old photographs in my stories. My husband has two large boxes filled with photographs from the 1930's and 1940's. He has no idea who they are, and everyone who might know them is now gone. At least write names on the back of your photographs. How many of us say we intend to preserve this history, but few of us actually do it?

Six Reasons to Preserve Our Life Stories

1. It is a way of preserving our parents and grandparents' life stories, honoring them, and passing this priceless heritage on to our grandchildren and great-grandchildren before it is lost forever.
2. It is a remembrance of historical times and what life was like then. We can pass this on to our grandchildren and tell how we got through these difficult times. This can teach them about overcoming when they face tough times in their lives.
3. It is an opportunity to remember happy times and preserve them forever. It tells our grandchildren who we were and helps them understand who they are.
4. It is a way of bringing families closer together in communication and understanding.
5. It is an opportunity to look back and gain perspective on the meaning of our lives.
6. It is the greatest gift we can give our children, grandchildren, great grandchildren, and ourselves.

Tips For Writing Your Life Story

Don't expect perfection. If we wait on perfection, nothing ever happens. It's like the Nike slogan, "Just do it." In the beginning, don't worry about spelling, grammar, or punctuation. All that can come later. The important thing is to allow your thoughts to flow and get the information down or into a tape recorder.

The reason some people don't write a life story is because there are painful things they don't want to include. *You don't have to include everything!* It is *your choice* what you include. You don't have to include anything you want to leave out.

Don't worry about information you don't have. We can get hung up on this and never move forward. If you lack information about your grandfather or don't know dates of birth, it is okay. Just write down what you know. If you want to do additional searching after you have everything else done, you can. The idea is to include the information you have.

Do one thing at a time. How do you eat an elephant? The answer: One bite at a time. You can't tackle everything at once. It is too overwhelming and we get lost. Don't overwhelm yourself. Do what is reasonable for you. Answer only one question, part of a question, or topic at a time. For example, write about only one of your children at one sitting. Or write about one best memory per day. Then lay your work aside until the next day when you again only tackle one question or issue.

Decide when it is best for you to write or record. It may be twenty or thirty minutes per day or three days per week. It helps to have a regularly scheduled time.

Don't give up! There are times we all feel stuck. You may need to lay your work aside for a *brief* period of time. You may be expecting too much of yourself. Maybe an hour three times per week is too much? Twenty minutes may be better for you. *Are you trying to be perfect,* rather than just preserving the memories and information? There may be something you need to skip over until later or leave out. Ask someone for help with punctuation or your area of difficulty. Think about how much it would mean to you to truly know who your grandmother was. Then remember, your story will someday mean as much to your grandchildren. It helps tell them who they are. ***Remember, before it's too late!***

Writing Your Life Story

There are many ways to write your life story. There are various formats on the Internet. This sheet talks about some ways to get started. It is a brief version. My information is copyrighted so this is for your personal use only. Do not expect perfection. At this point, don't worry much about spelling or punctuation. ***Remember, you do not have to discuss any area you do not want to discuss.***

1. For each of your significant family members, especially grandparents and parents (and later on each of your children and grandchildren), record their names, dates and places of birth, nationalities, education, occupations, and important historical times in which they lived. Write about what each was like as a person and your significant memories of them.
2. What were you like as a child? What are your best childhood memories?
3. What is your education?
4. Write about your work life.
5. Write about your spouse and wedding. How did you meet him or her and what attracted you? What have been the highlights of your lives together?
6. What historical times have you lived through?
7. Now is the time to write about your children, including the information listed above. Write about each child, their talents and accomplishments. What are you best memories about raising your children? What about each child are you most proud?
8. What role has religion or spirituality played in your life?
9. What are your talents and accomplishments?
10. Do you want to write about your struggles and how you overcame them?
11. What lessons about life have you learned that you would like to pass on to your grandchildren and great grandchildren?
12. What would you like to do with the time you have left?

Another way to write your life story is to write about the ten people or events that most influenced you to be who you are today. Who and what shaped you to be who you are?

It is vital to preserve one's family history, life story, and memories for the generations to come. I encourage everyone to either do this yourself or by enlisting the help of family or a friend. If you are unable to write your story, there are professionals who offer this service, which you may be able to locate on the Internet. You can also visit my website www.legacies.us for more information.

25.

End-of-Life Issues:
Avoiding an End-of-Life Crisis

What Are We Thinking?

I recently had a conversation with an aging friend. I refer to myself, at sixty-two, as being in the early stages of aging. My friend is in her early seventies and still quite active. She holds multiple, high profile positions and once assured me that she was "not going to go gently into the night." She fully agreed that people do better in their own homes. She also agreed that there is nothing simple about getting old and dying.

I believe in staying connected with our children and allowing them to help us through the aging process. I adamantly believe that we need an end-of-life advocate and if we have children, one of them is our best advocate. This, however, is very complex and requires a lot of thought and patience from both elder and adult child. Many times the elder is his or her own worst enemy in this process.

There are some key factors to consider.

(1) It is the elder's wishes we must consider, not our own.

(2) We should never rob anyone of their independence and dignity.

The advocate must make a commitment to carry out the elder's wishes as long as they are possible, legal and moral. These wishes should be stated long in advance of the end-of-life.

My mother completed her advance directive eight years before her death. Her basic wish to remain in her home never changed. There were many occasions when we could have gotten off course. As she aged, Mom lost total perspective of what and how much care she required. As we searched for caregivers, she repeatedly insisted Dad had been there for years and was still all the care she needed. Of course, some days Dad didn't function well either. He was the same age and also breaking down. The scenario of him being all she needed to stay home was a recipe for disaster. They both would have ended up in the rest home.

They were not capable of making safe, sound decisions that would assure both their wishes and their well-being. My siblings believed that Mom and Dad would only be safe and well cared for in a nursing home. Our parents never wavered from their desire to remain home, together until the end. They no longer were capable; yet, that desire was always present.

What Would You Want?

I'm an advocate of quality of life rather than quantity of life. We extend the lives of the elderly through modern medical miracles. Is it in their best interests? What would you want?

I believe it is possible that some time extensions can simply function to create medical revenue. I believe enormous health care institutions must be fed; after all, the bigger the monster, the larger the appetite. Think about the bottom line of what we really are accomplishing.

Most people tell me that they would rather be dead than in the rest home (skilled nursing, etc.). I've spoken to multiple senior groups and begin each talk with the question, "How many of you want to end your life in a nursing home?" To date, no one has said that this is their goal.

Most elders are caring, sharing, very good people;

people who have been a help both to their families and so-ciety. They are people who have earned the right to decide where they live and where they are going to die.

To keep adult children from feeling responsible or guilty, I believe we sometimes make end-of-life decisions based on our feelings rather than those of our older loved ones. There are emergency room activities that save an older person's life for a few hours, days, or even a couple of months. Is this what your loved one wants? This gener-ally leads to discharge to skilled nursing facilities or nursing homes. Is this a quality of life with which they would want to end their days? Is it what you would want for yourself? Is this a success, or is it prolonging their pain? What we've actually done is take a person who has lived a good life and sentenced them to a few days or a few months in the very place they feared most. What a reward!

An Example

We recently visited an elderly couple obviously in need of care. We were contacted by their daughter Kathy who set up the visit. John and Betty are in their nineties and have been married over fifty years. Kathy is in her early seventies and was providing as much care as they possibly could although the situation continued to deteriorate.

When we visited, we observed a very thin man who would have been about 6' 2" in his younger years. John was somewhat "stooped" and dressed in slippers and a torn bath robe, which allowed his extremely thin shoulder to protrude. During our visit, his wife, Betty, did not enter the room. The family described Betty as frail and weighing approximately 65 pounds. She was about 5'8" tall in her earlier years. As I observed the surroundings, it was a dimly lit, cluttered older home. The people had lived, at this once very nice location, for many years. I'm sure, in earlier times, the house and sur-rounding grounds were beautiful. There was a nice wooded view. It had originally been safe and functional as their residence.

Their daughter informed me that they would eat food she prepared only when she was present. If she prepared food and left it, they wouldn't even take it from the refrigerator. She reported that if she was not there to feed them, they would only drink beer and eat cookies. Her schedule only allowed time for three or four visits per week. She reported that other family members were only able to be minimally involved.

I asked the old fellow how he was doing. John told me how much they liked their home and that they were very comfortable and happy. He was obviously thin so I asked about their eating habits. He told me all the things they ate: toast, cereal, bacon, eggs and juice for breakfast every day and a variety of other food items throughout the day. There did not appear to be adequate food available to support his answer. Also, his physical appearance was that of someone starving, not robustly eating three meals per day. For the most part, he answered all the questions concerning their care in a manner that indicated there should be no intervention. His appearance did not match his answers.

I remembered my own father, when interviewed by outsiders, as always seeming bright, charming and able to provide the "right" answers to questions about their well-being. I knew my father's answers to be inaccurate even though the interviewer was generally fooled. I viewed my Dad as a "show dog." When he thought his or Mom's existence was threatened, he "put on a show" trying to convince people to leave them alone.

Based on the family's input and my own observations, this man was definitely a "show dog." He had all the right answers although there was no basis in fact to back them up. He obviously was in need of help with cooking, cleaning, and household organization to make the home safer. The family indicated that a Social Worker had "hot lined" them to the State Department of Health and Senior Services. He refused our help by saying, "I'll keep your card and call if I ever need anything." I explained that without help someone may try to remove them and he said, "I'll fight them."

As this episode progresses, the Social Worker did file a motion for guardianship. I spoke with her and she felt they were in imminent danger. The interesting part of this is that it takes approximately sixty to ninety days to get guardianship. I guess "imminent" means different things to different agencies. If Kathy was for some reason not able to continue care, John and Betty could starve to death before any mandated intervention. If they were children, they would have been removed from their home, nourished, medicated, and cared for until satisfactory living arrangements could be made.

Old people have the right of self-determination however, and they were electing to withdraw and die. Their daughter was adamantly and emphatically in favor of keeping them in their home. She just wanted them correctly nourished and safe. Her problem, however, was their needs were growing while her ability to help was diminishing, and she needed help. Kathy recognized that malnourished people have a difficult time with simple decisions. They no longer had the ability to process the reality of their situation. Some form of intervention was necessary.

A Social Worker assigned to them recommended four hours per day supplemental care and the elimination of driving privileges in order for them to remain at their home. They refused the care plan and the situation deteriorated to the point that Kathy was appointed their Guardian by the Court.

The Medical Model

Our area had a major ice storm in January. Due to a major power outage, the elderly couple moved into a nursing home. Prior to this event, they were at home. The time frame consisted of moving to the nursing home in mid-January and then the daughter's request to return them home at the end of March. They were out of their home no more than six weeks. Prior to these events, they had lived in the same home for more than forty years.

As their story unfolds, the couple had not been apart overnight for their entire fifty plus years of marriage. The rules of the nursing home were restrictive. I believe they were originally allowed to be together and then separated at a later time. Betty is docile and less mentally alert than her husband, who was reasonably functional at ninety years old. When I visited with him a couple of months earlier, I thought he was experiencing mild dementia. His desire was to stay with his wife, care for her, and protect her. As the nursing home staff attempted to take control of them, John became agitated. At one point, they found Betty on the floor and thought John may have shoved her. No one saw what happened. We later learned that Betty "faints," lies on the floor, for attention. They were separated and John became even more agitated. He demanded that Betty be returned to their room and threatened to strike the staff. Due to John's aggressive behavior, he was moved to a local hospital for a psychiatric evaluation. Now, he and his wife of over fifty years were not even in the same building. His wife and partner, who had always been at his side, was no longer with him. Of course, he was agitated! At the hospital, John became aggressive and needed to be restrained. The doctor chemically restrained him. His psychiatric evaluation indicated a reasonably healthy ninety year old male with mild dementia. The hospital indicated that John was not capable of returning home. The staff stated that, if John returned home against medical advice, they would not treat him in the future.

Meanwhile, Betty was sleeping her life away at the nursing home. She grieved for her husband and wanted to be home with him.

Kathy, their daughter and guardian, who wanted only to help, was saddened by the tragedy of these unfolding events. Nursing home staff told Kathy that Betty can't function outside the nursing home and, if removed, the doctor would drop her as a patient.

Did I mention that John and Betty were private pay patients? They had plenty of money and there was no problem collecting fees from them. In my opinion, this is the nursing home, medical model "cash cow," and I believe they didn't want to lose it! In my wife's opinion, medical personnel or social workers may have done what current conventional opinion truly thought was in their best interests. My question is, "Whose interests?" I faced this same situation when I removed my Mother from a nursing home. Mom was "private" pay and the Social Worker in charge of her care was adamant that, if I took her home, she would surely perish. The point of this book is not to criticize conventional wisdom, it is to change it.

Assisted Living at Home

Kathy contracted our company to provide twenty-four hour, seven days per week, non-medical care in their home. Our caregiver prepares meals, does laundry, cleans the house, transports them to the doctor, and shops with them. She provides whatever they need to stay at home. We prompt the taking of medications and assist with any activities of daily living that cause them difficulty. The patient-to-caregiver ratio is two to one. In the best hospitals or nursing homes, the ratio is far greater. In their home, John and Betty will not wait for a glass of water or to be taken to the bathroom. There is no waiting for personal care. They will be on their own schedule rather than the schedule of the institution. When they require health care, it will be delivered by home health nursing agencies at the direction of their doctor. Medicare pays for medically necessary services.

John and Betty will share the same bed. Sounds pretty dangerous, doesn't it! That's what the hospital and nursing home indicated. How dare you attempt to reunite them and take them home? Just who do you think you are? In their professional opinions, John and Betty would be better off doped into compliance; sad, lonely, grieving, confused, agitated, angry and separated until their deaths.

If they were dying of another cause such as cancer (other than aging), Hospice would rush in and promote the virtues of being able to die in your own home. Why does this change when the cause of death is aging? Why does living a long and productive life commit us to being tortured at the end of our lives? Separating us from our life partner, moving us to unfamiliar surroundings, drugging us into compliance and controlling us sure sounds the way I want to end up! How about you? It appears that the medical community wants us to extend our lives even though it may be torturous! Why? They get money for hospice. They get money for extending life. If you use a less expensive non-medical provider and stay in your home, the medical monster doesn't get fed!

What Would You Want for Your Dog?

Think about this scenario. You have a really nice old dog at home. You love this dog. His name is Skippy. He is your ever faithful companion. He meets you at the door, barks and scares away the bad guys. He understands when you are down, and he's your buddy. Skippy loves bones so you regularly give him a big steak bone as a treat and watch him peacefully chew on it. Do you have the picture? Peaceful, loving, maybe a fire in the background, and you have your arm around someone you love. Admittedly, Skippy is old and gradually breaking down. He's not as tolerant as he once was.

Then someone takes Skippy's bone away. He growls

with displeasure. The meter reader hears the growl, decides the dog needs to go to the veterinarian for an evaluation, and reports Skippy. Skippy is at the veterinary hospital in terrifying surroundings. This is a place that in the past always made him nervous. People are poking on him, prodding, and testing him. Skippy becomes protective, aggressive, and shows anger. He growls, barks and tries to bite those he sees as aggressors. The veterinarian observes Skippy's behavior and records that he is mean-spirited, aggressive, vicious, and likely to bite if returned home. The recommendation is: Keep Skippy confined to the kennel and charge the owner for his care until he dies.

Skippy doesn't understand why he can't just go home, lay by his owner, and chew his favorite bone. Skippy is now placed in long-term doggy care. The kennels are brightly painted, well lit, with small bedding spaces. Skippy can see out but he can't go out unless accompanied by a handler. There isn't adequate staff to allow this very often. His water dish is often empty and the kennel fills with waste. He is fed regularly, although the food is an institutional quality dog food. It is not the special Skippy food he enjoyed at home. And, of course, there are no longer bones to chew. The people are nice although obviously overworked and probably underpaid. They don't seem to really understand much about older dogs. There is a smell of urine and heavy deodorants to cover the smell. Dogs from each of the other kennels continually bark for services but, due to staffing levels, they must wait their turn.

Skippy is now surrounded by other dogs who want to be at home with their bones. These dogs are aggravated, bark continually, and are very unhappy. They have also been classified as vicious. Each dog is trying to get out and wants to be left alone with his bone one more time. Finally, Skippy figures out that the only thing he can still control is his appetite. He is miserable. His body knows that if he eats less, the end will be closer. Skippy views his future confinement with no hope. His loving owner now rarely visits because it is so sad. After all, the veterinarian says that this is the absolute best care for Skippy and he is happy here. As Skippy whimpers and wastes away, the veterinarian makes his condition a persuasive point to his loving owner. "Skippy is so far gone that you couldn't possibly provide the necessary care at home."

Skippy is now thin, drawn, lost, and lonely. Death seems to be the only friend that remains. Skippy has ended up in a strange, antiseptic place; the place he feared most. He is separated from his family and surrounded by other dogs who also feel discarded. After all, they are better off, aren't they?

Skippy cries, "Why can't I go find my big bone in the sky?" The veterinarian keeps forcing food and medicine into him. Gee, this is a great place for him, and we must extend this wonderful quality of life for as long as possible! Skippy dreams of his days on the floor chewing his bone with his owner nearby. "What have I done to deserve this?"

In this scenario, most of us would demand our dog back. We would do whatever it took to bring Skippy home even though the veterinarian told us it was a terrible mistake and Skippy would surely die.

What Do You Want?

We all know in our hearts that death is not the worst thing that can happen to us. We hold the power to artificially extend Skippy's little doggy life. We can make the decision to force Skippy to live a tortured extended life. Why? How is it better to force Skippy to live the life he did not choose, to die in the way he had feared in a strange, lonely, antiseptically clean, non-loving environment. After all, what dog would want to die at home with his favorite bone, surrounded by loved ones and his fondest memories? How could a loving owner make this possible when all the experts disagree?

I can tell you how! It takes a tremendous amount of love, commitment, time, resources, and emotional effort, but it can be done. It takes a commitment to treat others as you want to be treated. It was sure easier to buy the veterinarian's story about how much better off Skippy would be. Someday, someone is going to make the same decision for you. Why do we take a different stand with an aging loved one? Aren't the elderly as deserving as our pets? Where are the "quality of life" people for the elderly? Why do we extend life against our wishes? I'm not talking about suicide. I'm talking about the natural end-of-life. One reason is the idea of saving lives is so ingrained that we forget what a meaningful life truly is.

26.
Facing Death

Face to face with death! No, not your own. We are going to die at some point; we all die. Getting older is definitely a terminal disease. Being born is a death sentence; we just don't know how long until the sentence is carried out. We talk of people going to the other side, crossing over, reaping the great reward, finally at rest, peace at last, back with family, finally home; all easy terms for our end. We also use the short terms; goner, dead, deceased, bought the farm, croaked.

My Dad's favorite joke in his last years was that of the little boy asking his grandfather if he could make a noise like a frog. Grandpa asks the boy, "Why" and the reply is, "I heard Mommy telling Daddy that as soon as grandpa croaks, we'd all go to Hawaii." Funny thing is, Dad survived Mom and the year after Dad died, I took my family to Hawaii in his memory.

As I began the care-giving process with my parents, Mom would say, "I'm just an old lady who has lived too long." You know; we rush into a situation to make it better, to keep some dread circumstance from occurring. We're here to save Mom and Dad! We can't. We may extend their lives; but from aging, we can't save them. I believe in the quality of life, not quantity of life. I see adult children pull out all the stops to keep Mom alive, especially with extremely restrictive diets. Now, I am not advocating ignoring diet and exercise. A Licensed Nursing Home Administrator recently told me that accident prevention along with proper rest and nourishment would keep most people in their own homes to the end. On the other hand, if today were your last day, what would you do, what would you give up, how would you like to be treated? Mom was ninety; any day could be her last day. How strict should I be?

My son is a Registered Nurse and was working the emergency room while Mom and Dad were aged. He told me about ambulances bringing in very frail elderly people in the process of dying, and the families doing all they could to save them. CPR involves chest compressions that can break ribs. Some life saving techniques can be brutal. You need to be aware that you can bag them, tube them, compress them, empty their stomachs, put in I.V.'s; you can do a lot. Maybe they'll live another three days, who knows? How would you want to be treated? Do you know how your parent wants to be treated? Have you asked or had a conversation with them about their end-of-life wants and desires? They know they are going to die. They are getting a much closer look. Their parents, some friends, maybe siblings have died. It is often on their minds! They want to talk about it. If they're okay with it, why aren't you? They will get some peace from the knowledge that things have been "taken care of."

My Mom had an advance directive expressing her desire to receive no services to extend her life; not food, not water, nothing. Her belief was that she was an old lady who had lived a very good life, had a wonderful family, but had lived too long.

Her two greatest pleasures in life at the end of her life were watching Matlock and Judge Judy. She was ready to go and wanted nothing to stand in the way. She had great love for her husband of sixty-six years and for her children. She was concerned about how Dad would do without her but, in her heart, she knew we would care for him. She was at peace! You know how I know? I talked to her in detail about these things.

I asked her doctor to go over all her options, in my

presence, with her. I clearly knew what her end-of-life wishes were. Her doctor was involved and committed to fulfilling her end-of-life wishes. I knew this from multiple conversations beginning a year and one-half from when she actually died. I posted her advance directive on the refrigerator with instructions. I went, time and time again, over them with Dad. For all these years, Mom and Dad had their method of communication and he knew exactly what she wanted. I learned that, if in an emergency an ambulance arrives, the paramedics are duty bound to save the life. You won't do any good waving the advance directive; they are bound to save the life. I asked Mom's doctor what to do in an emergency. His answer was to call him, not the ambulance.

Life works in funny ways. I was married to a woman for thirty-four years who helped with my parents' care. Judy was loving and nurturing to them even though I'm not sure they earned the treatment. We hadn't had much to do with my parents until they needed additional care and for some reason Judy really took them under her wing. She was struggling with the effects of COPD, diabetes, and bouts with pancreatitis. At one point during caring for my parents, she was hospitalized for ninety days. After release, she continued on abdominal feeding for an additional six months while at home. I actually spent two years caring for my wife and my parents.

On Thanksgiving in 2001, Mom had a stroke which we all thought would be fatal. On the way home from what we thought were our goodbyes, my wife cried and pleaded with me to do something to save my mother. I was feeling the pain of the potential loss and the desire to do something to save my mother. I was an emotional train wreck looking for a place to happen. What I ultimately did was exactly what my mother had wanted. I said goodbye and waited for the end. Life is funny. For some reason, after about three days, Mom revived and perked back up. However, she was disappointed that God hadn't taken her. Not angry, just disappointed.

Unexpectedly on December 18, 2001, my wife Judy died. I thought telling Mom of Judy's death would kill her; it didn't. She just looked kind of bewildered and felt sad for me. I think she knew now she would have a friend in heaven. I think it made passing easier for her. Life is funny, it also can be pretty sad if you let it.

In mid-January of 2002, I stopped to visit Mom and Dad. They were eating their supper and having a very pleasant meal. I offered Mom a spoonfull of mashed potatoes and, as she was chewing, she choked and spit them back into the spoon. Her head moved slightly, but not violently, and she frowned. I asked if she was okay and her reply was that she was tired and going to bed. Our full-time caregiver helped her to bed. The next morning, it became apparent that she had had a stroke. She knew where she was and who was there but she had lost the ability to swallow. The doctor told me we would give it some time to see if she recovered again. In a couple of days, he prescribed a morphine patch to ease what pain she might be feeling. I watched my father frantically trying to get her to drink anything to help his sweetheart stay with him. I saw his pain, felt his pain, and knew his pain. He was frantic, yet never wavered. We both knew her wishes. We both had heard her desires.

Knowing this was probably the end, I phoned the doctor and asked what to do? He told me to call the funeral home when it was over. There was no need for an ambulance and no need to extend her life for a few more days. My sister was with her at the end and said she saw Mom's spirit dancing on the way to heaven. It was sad, but also happy. Mom's at peace. She went the way she wanted to go. You know how I know? She told me face-to-face a year and one-half before she died. It is important for us to ask and be sure we know!

I am reminded of a story my doctor told me years

218

ago. It seems a man visits his doctor for a physical. The doctor asks all the usual questions; "Do you smoke, do you drink, do you eat junk foods, chase wild women, etc.?" When the man returns for his results, as you might suspect, the doc tells him he must stop all his bad habits; no smoking, no drinking, etc. The man then asks the doc, "Will I live any longer?" The doctor's reply was "No, but it will sure seem like it."

My point is, go face-to-face, person to person with your parents and know how they want to finish their earthly lives. Talk to them about death and dying. Know their faith, expectations, wants, wishes, and fears. Life is funny. You only get to die once. The person dying should have some say in how they go. After all, it's their event!

A tip worth repeating; make decisions and actions so at the funeral you're okay with what you've done. Many spiritual people believe death is a beginning, not the end. Many non-spiritual people still remark that the deceased is "better off, free from pain, at rest." If we truly believe our own words, grieving is us feeling sorrow for ourselves.

We may feel that keeping someone alive regardless of their wishes absolves us of guilt. What would the individual truly want?

Money is also another issue. There is a lot of money (public, private and through insurance) for Hospice programs. There is private or public money for nursing homes. There isn't substantial health care money to be made by allowing us to die a natural death in our homes. In the future this will change. Baby boomers will spend their money on goods and services to stay at home. After all, it is a lot less expensive and we actually get to use our resources for our own good. It is not about how long we live. It's about *how* we live.

In the famous Terri Schiavo case, her life was extended nearly fifteen years. Why? Her end-of-life was headline news for a long period of time. Complete strangers

219

frantically tried to "keep her alive." Congress even got involved in *her* end-of-life decisions. Why? People cried on TV. Preachers prayed. The very people who tell us what a wonderful place heaven is and how going home to God is the ultimate final reward prayed for her to live. Why? Of all the millions of people crying, praying, bringing suit, legislating, reporting, and writing, did you hear people express desire to have their lives extended in this way? No! Did you read or hear of anyone who said they would trade places with Terri Schiavo? Have you ever, in your life, heard anyone express an interest in being kept on artificial life support, in total unconsciousness, with no possibility of recovery for as long as possible? *I doubt it!*

Missouri was involved in a landmark end-of-life case involving Nancy Cruzan . *"*Nancy Beth Cruzan (July 20, 1957–December 26, 1990) was a figure in the right-to-die movement. After an auto accident left her in a persistent vegetative state, her family fought in courts for three years, as far as the U.S. Supreme Court, to have her feeding tube removed. The Court denied the family's request citing lack of evidence of Cruzan's wishes, but the family ultimately prevailed by providing additional evidence. On December 14, 1990, the tube was removed and she died 12 days later."* *(Copied from Wikipedia).*

The following is downloaded from the Legal Services of Missouri web site. (www.lsmo.org)

Living Wills and Other Advance Directives

What is a Living Will?

A living will is a brief declaration or statement that a person may make indicating their desire that certain medical treatment be either withheld or withdrawn under certain circumstances. The Missouri statute authorizing the creation of living wills specifies that the statement or declaration be in substantially the following form:

"I have the primary right to make my own decisions concerning treatment that might unduly prolong the dying process. By this declaration I express to my physician, family and friends my intent. If I should have a terminal condition it is my desire that my dying not be prolonged by administration of death-prolonging procedures. If my condition is terminal and I am unable to participate in decisions regarding my medical treatment, I direct my attending physician to withhold or withdraw medical procedures that merely prolong the dying process and are not necessary to my comfort or to alleviate pain. It is not my intent to authorize affirmative or deliberate acts or omissions to shorten my life, rather only to permit the natural process of dying."

How is a Living Will Made?

Any competent person 18 years of age or older can make a living will by signing and dating a statement similar to that shown above before two witnesses. These witnesses must be at least 18 years old, and should not be related to the person signing the declaration, a beneficiary of his or her estate or financially responsible for his or her medical care. The statement can be typed or handwritten. It is recommended that a living will or any other advance directives be considered and prepared in advance of any hospitalization or impending surgery it is not something anyone should feel pressured to decide in a short period of time, if that can be avoided.

Limitations of Living Wills

While most people have heard of living wills, many are unaware of the significant limitations of the living will as defined by Missouri statutes. The terms "death-prolonging procedure" and "terminal condition" are used in the statute to specify the circumstances to which a living will applies.

The statute defines both of those terms as relating to a condition where death will occur within a short period of time whether or not certain treatment is provided. In other words, the patient will die shortly with or without artificial resuscitation, use of a ventilator, artificially supplied nutrition and hydration or other invasive surgical procedures. By definition, then, a living will only avoids treatment when death is imminent and the treatment is ineffective to avoid or significantly delay death. Furthermore, the statute prohibits a living will from withholding or withdrawing artificially supplied nutrition and hydration, which is sustenance supplied through a feeding tube or IV.

Alternatives to Living Wills

For patients who desire to give instructions for their health care which exceed the limitations of the living will statute, there is an alternative, commonly referred to as "advance directives." An advance directive is an instruction by a patient as to the withholding or withdrawing of certain medical treatment in advance of the patient suffering a condition which renders the patient unable to refuse such treatment. A competent patient always has the right to refuse treatment for himself or herself or direct that such treatment be discontinued. Without an advance directive, once a patient becomes incapacitated, he or she may well lose that right. A living will is simply one type of advance directive. Recent court cases have made it clear that people have the right to make other types of advance directives which exceed the limitations of the living will statute. Those directives need to be "clear and convincing," and may include instructions to withhold or withdraw artificially supplied nutrition and hydration or other treatment or machinery which may maintain a patient in a persistent vegetative state. These expanded advance directives can be tailored to meet the needs and desires of each individual patient, and need not be in any standard form. For example, they can specify that certain procedures are to be used for a reasonable period of time and then discontinued if they do not prove to be effective. Generally, additional advance directives should be signed, dated and witnessed in the same manner as living wills.

You will find a copy of The Missouri Bar's Durable Power of Attorney for Health Care and Health Care Directive at www. lsom.org then click on Legal Self Help link on left hand side of page then click the health care symbol for multiple forms and information.

What Should I do With My Living Will?

The most important part of having a living will or other advance directives after they are signed is to be certain that they are accessible. They should be kept close at hand, not in a safe deposit box, because they may be needed at a Moment's notice. Many people travel with them. Some even keep them in their purse or billfold. At a minimum, it is recommended that you deliver a copy to your attending physician and at least make your close relatives aware that you have one. Giving a copy of your living will or other advance directives to your physician gives you an opportunity to discuss your desires and ask any questions you may have about any procedure and also to ask your physician if he or she will follow your directions. If you have appointed an attorney-in-fact to make health care decisions in case of your incapacity, he or she should have a copy. If you are hospitalized, a copy should go into your medical records. For these reasons, it is often wise to sign more than one copy of your living will or other advance directives.

Revoking a Living Will

Once made, a living will or other advance directives are easily revoked or cancelled. They can be revoked either orally or in writing. If possible, it is advisable to gather and destroy all copies of the advance directives if you desire to revoke them. By statute, health care providers are required to note a revocation of a living will in the medical records of the patient.

Durable Power of Attorney

If you have a durable power of attorney which appoints someone to make health care decisions for you, do you still need a living will or other advance directives? The answer is yes. Whether or not you have a power of attorney does not affect the need or desire for a living will or other advance directives. If you do not have a power of attorney, your advance directives will be very helpful to instruct your physician and the hospital as to the care you desire. If you do have a power of attorney, your advance directives will give very important guidance to your attorney-in-fact as to how he or she should act. In fact, you may want to combine your power of attorney, your living will and your other advance directives into one document.

Why Give Advance Directives?

You accomplish at least two things by giving advance directives, regardless of whether they direct all possible treatment, no treatment or only some treatment. First, you ensure that the treatment you receive is the treatment you desire, no more and no less. Second, you take the burden off of your family and friends to make those decisions for you at a time when they will most likely be emotionally upset by your critical condition. Finally, you may be avoiding litigation to determine what treatment you really desired or intended. In any event, it is time well spent.

Eric's Comments

My writings are not intended to offer legal advice. I refer and add information from Legal Services of Southern Missouri (www.lsmo.org) as a possible source for further information.

There is nothing simple about aging and dying. Advice from counselors, pastoral help, hospice organizations and other sources may be helpful as well.

In our area there is an active organization called "Community Alliance for Compassionate Care at the End-of-life" which deals with end-of-life issues. Remember, we can't control when our lives end. We owe it to our loved ones to make our end-of-life wishes known. Don't leave that overwhelming burden to them!

You will find a copy of The Missouri Bar's Durable Power of Attorney for Health Care and Health Care Directive at www.lsmo.org, then click on Legal Self Help link on left hand side of page, then click the health care symbol for multiple forms and information. The following is a copy downloaded from this site:

DURABLE POWER OF ATTORNEY FOR HEALTH CARE AND HEALTH CARE DIRECTIVE

Question and Answers, Instructions and Sample Form

Distributed as a public service by

The Missouri Bar

Durable Power of Attorney For Health Care
and
Health Care Directive

Published by The Missouri Bar

Read the Questions and Answers and Instructions which accompany this form carefully before attempting to complete the Durable Power of Attorney for Health Care and Health Care Directive. This form is not the only way to express your desires regarding future health care. This form is distributed with the understanding that The Missouri Bar, its committees, authors and speakers do not thereby render legal advice. If you do not understand this form, or if you feel the form does not meet your needs, you should consult a lawyer.

This form belongs to:

Name: _____

Address: _____

_____

_____

Telephone: _____

Social Security Number: _____

Medicare Number: _____

QUESTIONS AND ANSWERS CONCERNING THE DURABLE POWER OF ATTORNEY FOR HEALTH CARE AND HEALTH CARE DIRECTIVE

INTRODUCTION

Many Missouri citizens are concerned about the health care they may receive if they cannot express their desires. The Missouri Bar is providing this form to you as a public service. This form is not the only way to express your desires regarding future health care. If you have special needs, you may want to consult a lawyer. This form allows you to appoint an agent to make health care decisions if you are unable to do so. The form also allows you to furnish clear and convincing proof of your intentions regarding your future health care.

QUESTIONS AND ANSWERS

The following questions and answers may help you understand the form:

Do I need a lawyer to complete this form?
A. No. However, if you do not feel this form meets your needs, you may want to consult a lawyer.

Why does this form have three parts?
A. Part I is your Durable Power of Attorney for Health are. It allows you to appoint someone to make decisions for you if you are unable to act concerning your health care.

Part II is your Health Care Directive. It allows you to express your intention regarding your future health care.

Part III provides for notarization. If you intend to use the Durable Power of Attorney For Health Care in Part I, this document must be notarized.

What is a Durable Power of Attorney for Health Care (Part I)?

A. It is a document that allows you to appoint someone to make all kinds of health care decisions for you, but only if you are not able to do so. These decisions may include, but are not limited to, decisions to withhold or withdraw life-prolonging procedures.

What is a Health Care Directive (Part II)?

A. It is like a living will; it is a document that allows you to state in advance your wishes regarding the use of life-prolonging procedures. It may be relied upon when you are unable to communicate your decisions.

Do I need both?

A. If you decide that you want someone to speak for you concerning your future health care you will need to fill out the Durable Power of Attorney for Health Care (Part I). Please consider doing this if there is someone you would like to appoint. If you decide that you want to express your desires about life-prolonging procedures you will need to fill out the Health Care Directive (Part II). The Directive will provide doctors and others with evidence concerning your wishes. The Health Care Directive (Part II) may also serve as a guide for your agent.

Does the person I appoint as my agent have to be a lawyer?

A. No. You may appoint a person 18 years of age or older. An agent is usually a close relative or someone you trust with your life. It cannot be your doctor, an employee of your doctor, or an owner/operator or employee of a health care facility in which you are a resident, unless you are related.

Can an agent withhold or withdraw artificially supplied nutrition and hydration?
A. Yes, if you specifically authorize your agent to do so. The Durable Power of Attorney for Health Care (Part I) requires that you indicate whether or not you want your agent to have authority to withdraw this type of medical treatment. The Health Care Directive (Part II) also requires hat you indicate whether or not you want artificially supplied nutrition and hydration to be withheld or withdrawn under certain circumstances.

When can my agent act?
A. The Durable Power of Attorney for Health Care (Part I) only become effective when you are incapacitated and unable to make health care decisions. Unless you state otherwise, Missouri law requires two doctors to make the incapacity decision. The form allows you to choose whether you would like one or two doctors to make the incapacity decision.

If I already have a Durable Power of Attorney, should I sign a Durable Power of Attorney for Health Care (Part I)?
A. Possibly. Your existing Durable Power of Attorney may not cover health care or comply with Missouri Durable Power of Attorney for Health Care Act.

If I already have a Living Will, should I sign a Health Care Directive (Part II)?
A. Possibly. Many Living Will forms currently in use only apply when you are expected to die within a short period of time and do not allow for the withdrawal or withholding of artificial nutrition and hydration. They do not cover a condition such as the persistent vegetative state which occurred in the well known case of Cruzan v. Director, 110 S.Ct. 2841 (1990).

DURABLE POWER OF ATTORNEY FOR HEALTH CARE
AND
HEALTH CARE DIRECTIVE

This form allows you to express your desires concerning your health care.

The Durable Power of Attorney for Health Care (Part I) allows you to appoint an agent to make health care decisions if you are unable to do so.

The Health Care Directive (Part II) allows you to furnish clear and convincing proof of your intentions regarding withholding or withdrawal of life-prolonging procedures, and may be relied upon by your physician even if you are unable to communicate your decisions.

The General Provisions (Part III) apply to both the Directive and the Power of Attorney. You may complete the Power of Attorney (Part I) or the Directive (Part II) or both.

IF THERE IS A STATEMENT WITH WHICH YOU DO NOT AGREE, YOU MAY CHANGE IT AND ADD YOUR INITIALS.

Read the Questions and Answers and Instructions which accompany this form carefully before attempting to complete the Durable Power of Attorney for Health Care and Health Care Directive. This form is not the only way to express your desires regarding future health care. This form is distributed with the understanding that The Missouri Bar, its committees, authors, and speakers do not thereby render legal advice. If you do not understand this form, or if you feel the form does not meet your needs, you should consult a lawyer.

General Instructions for Completing The Durable Power of Attorney for Health Care and Health Care Directive

Read the entire form before signing or initialing any part.

Discuss this form with your family and close friends. Include anyone who may be asked to make decisions concerning your future health care if you are unable to do so.

Give a copy of this form to your family, close friends, doctor, lawyer, minister or anyone that may be asked to make decisions concerning your health care if you are unable to do so. Do not place the original of this form in your safe deposit box. It will not be usable unless your agent or alternate agents have access to your safe deposit box without your presence through a signature card from the bank where the safe deposit box is located.

Decide whether you want to complete the Durable Power of Attorney for Health Care (Part I) and the Health Care Directive (Part II). You may choose to complete only one or both.

Instructions for Completing Part I

Durable Power of Attorney for Health Care

If you decide not to complete the Durable Power of Attorney for Health Care (Part I), write your initials above the line that says "initials" in the shaded box which appears below the words **"Part I. Durable Power of Attorney for Health Care"**.

If you decide to complete the Durable Power of Attorney for Health Care (Part I), please follow the instructions below.

DO NOT initial the shaded box below the words **"Part I. Durable Power of Attorney for Health Care"**.

Complete **Section 1 Selection of Agent** with the name, address, and telephone number of the person you choose as your agent.

If you wish to complete **Section 2 Alternate Agents** write the names, addresses, and telephone numbers of persons you would like to be your agent if the person you named in Section 1 is not available.

Part I. Durable Power of Attorney for Health Care

• **If you do NOT wish to name an agent to make health care decisions for you, write your initials in the box to the right and got to Part II.**

Initials

This form has been prepared to comply with the "Durable Power of Attorney for Health Care Act" of Missouri.

1. Selection of Agent. I appoint:
   Name: _____
   Address: _____
   _____
   Telephone: _____
   as my Agent.

> **It is suggested that only one Agent be named. However, if more than one Agent is named, any one may act individually unless you specify otherwise.**

2. **Alternate Agents.** Only an Agent named by me may act under this Durable Power of Attorney. If my Agent resigns or is not able or available to make health care decisions for me, of if an Agent named by me is divorced from me or is my spouse and legally separated from me, I appoint the person(s) named below (in the order named if more than one):

First Alternate Agent

Name: _____
Address: _____
_____
Telephone: _____

Second Alternate Agent

Name: _____
Address: _____
_____
Telephone: _____

> THIS IS A DURABLE POWER OF ATTORNEY, AND THE AUTHOR-ITY OF MY AGENT, WHEN EFFECTIVE, SHALL NOT TERMINATE OR BE VOID OR VOIDABLE IF I AM OR BECOME DISABLED OR INCAPACITATED OR IN THE EVENT OF LATER UNCERTAINTY AS TO WHETHER I AM DEAD OR ALIVE.

Instructions for Completing Part I. (Continued)

In Section 3 Effective Date and Durability the form lets you choose whether one or two doctors need to certify that you are incapacitated. Incapacitated means that you are no longer able to make decisions for yourself and it is time for your agent to act.

Choose whether you want one or two physicians to decide whether you are incapacitated.

If you want two doctors to decide that you are incapacitated, do not write anything in this section.

If you want one doctor to decide that you are incapacitated, write your initials in the shaded box above the line that says "initials" to the right of the statement "If you want one physician instead of two to decide whether you are incapacitated, write your initials in the box to the right." that is found in Section 3.

In Section 4 Agent's Powers you decide whether or not your agent can make decisions concerning withholding or withdrawing artificially supplied nutrition and hydration. Please indicate your decision in the space provided.

If you complete this Part I, you must sign it before a notary for it to be effective. Please look at the instructions on page 14.

Part I. Durable Power of Attorney for Health Care (Continued)

3. **Effective Date and Durability.** Except for such earlier dates as may be set forth in Section 4, below, this Durable Power of Attorney is effective when two physicians decide and certify that I am incapacitated and unable to make and communicate a health care decision.

• **If you want ONE physician, instead of TWO, to decide whether you are incapacitated, write your initials in the box to the right.**

4. Agent's Powers. I grant to my Agent full authority to:

A. Give consent to, prohibit or withdraw any type of health care, medical care, treatment or procedure, even if my death may result.

• **If you wish to AUTHORIZE your Agent to direct a health care provider to withhold or withdraw artificially supplied nutrition and hydration (including tube feeding of food and water), write your initials in the box to the right.**

• **If you DO NOT WISH TO AUTHORIZE your Agent to direct a health care provider to withhold or withdraw artificially supplied nutrition and hydration, (including tube feeding of food and water), write your initials in the box to the right.**

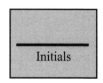

236

B. Make all necessary arrangements for health care services on my behalf, and to hire and fire medical personnel responsible for my care;

C. Move me into or out of any health care facility (even if against medical advice) to obtain compliance with the decisions of my Agent; and

D. Take any other action necessary to do what I authorize here, including (but not limited to) granting any waiver or release from liability required by any health care provider, and taking any legal action at the expense of my estate to enforce this Durable Power of Attorney.

E. Act, effective immediately, as my "personal representative" as defined in 45 C.F.R. § 164.502(g), the regulations enacted pursuant to the Health Insurance Portability and Accountability Act of 1996 ("HIPAA"), and as hereafter amended, for the purpose of authorizing the release of my complete health record as may be necessary in order to obtain for my benefit medical treatment or consultation.

5. **Agent's Financial Liability and Compensation.** My Agent acting under this Durable Power of Attorney will incur no personal financial liability. My Agent shall not be entitled to compensation for services performed under this Durable Power of Attorney, but my Agent shall be entitled to reimbursement for all reasonable expenses incurred as a result of carrying out any provision hereof.

Instruction for Completing Part II.

Health Care Directive

If you decide not to complete the Health Care Directive (Part II), write your initials above the line that says "initials" in the shaded box which appears below the words "Part II. Health Care Directive".

If you decide to complete the Health Care Directive (Part II), please follow the instructions below:

DO NOT initial the shaded box below the words **"Part II. Health Care Directive"**.

Read the Directive Carefully.

Review the list of life-prolonging procedures and decide which, if any, of these procedures you would like to have withheld or withdrawn. Write your initials next to each procedure you want to be withheld or withdrawn if you are persistently unconscious or there is no reasonable expectation of your recovery from a seriously incapacitating or terminal illness or condition.

Part II. Health Care Directive

• If you *DO NOT WISH* to make a health care directive, rite your initials in the box to the right, and go to Part III. I make this HEALTH CARE DIRECTIVE ("Di rective") to exercise my right to deter mine the course of my health care and to provide clear and convincing proof of my wishes and instructions about my treatment.

Initials

If I am persistently unconscious or there is no reasonable expectation of my recovery from a seriously incapacitating or terminal illness or condition, I direct that all of the life-prolonging procedures that I have initialled below be with held or withdrawn.

I want the following life-prolonging procedures to be withheld or withdrawn:

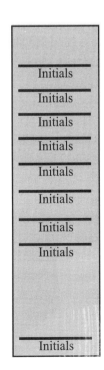

• artificially supplied nutrition and hydra tion (including tube feeding of food and water)

Initials

• surgery or other invasive procedures

Initials

• heart-lung resuscitation (CPR)

Initials

• antibiotic

Initials

• dialysis

Initials

• mechanical ventilator (respirator)

Initials

• chemotherapy

Initials

• radiation therapy

Initials

• all other "life-prolonging" medical or surgical procedures that are merelyin tended to keep me alive without reason able hope of improving my condition or curing my illness or injury ....

Initials

239

However, if my physician believes that any life-prolonging procedure may lead to a significant recovery, I direct my physician to try the treatment for a reasonable period of time. If it does not improve my condition, I direct the treatment be withdrawn even if it shortens my life. I also direct that I be given medical treatment to relieve pain or to provide comfort, even if such treatment might shorten my life, suppress my appetite or my breathing, or be habit-forming.

I want to donate my organs or tissues and realize it may be necessary to maintain my body artificially after my death on a breathing machine until my organs can be removed.

☐ Yes

☐ No

☐ I do not want to address this question now

IF I HAVE NOT DESIGNATED AN AGENT IN THE DURABLE POWER OF ATTORNEY, THIS DOCUMENT IS MEANT TO BE IN FULL FORCE AND EFFECT AS MY HEALTH CARE DIRECTIVE.

Instructions for Completing Part III.

General Provisions Included in the Directive and Durable Power of Attorney

Part III. <u>must be completed</u> for the Durable Power of Attorney for Health Care (Part I) and the Health Care Directive (Part II) to be effective. Please see the instructions on the back of the following page.

Part III. General Provisions Included in the Directive and Durable Power of Attorney

1. Relationship Between Directive and Durable Power of Attorney. If I have executed the Directive and the Durable Power of Attorney, I encourage my Agent to follow my wishes as expressed in the Directive in making decisions regarding life-prolonging procedures. However, I have confidence in my Agent's ability to make decisions in my best interest, and I authorize my Agent to make decisions that are contrary to my Directive in his or her best judgment. If the Durable Power of Attorney is somehow determined to be ineffective, or if my Agent is not able to serve, the Directive is intended to be used on its own as firm instructions to my health care
providers regarding life-prolonging procedures.

2. Protection of Third Parties Who Rely on My Agent. No person who relies in good faith upon any representations by my Agent or Alternate Agent shall be liable to me, my estate, my heirs or assigns, for recognizing the Agent's authority.

3. Revocation of Prior Directive or Durable Power of Attorney. I revoke any prior LIVING WILL, Declaration or Health Care Directive executed by me. If I have appointed an Agent in a prior durable power of attorney, I revoke any health care terms contained in that durable power of attorney.

4. Validity. This document is intended to be valid in any jurisdiction in which it is presented. The provisions of this document are separable, so that the invalidity of one or more provisions shall not affect any others. A copy of this document shall be as valid as the original.

Instructions for Completing Part III. (Continued)

Part III must be completed for the Durable Power of Attorney for Health Care (Part I) and the Health Care Directive (Part II) to be effective. Please follow the instructions below:

Sign and date in the space provided. Please print your name and address under the signature line.

Have two witnesses sign and write in their addresses on the lines provided.

If you have completed the Durable Power of Attorney for Health Care (Part I.), you will need to sign the form in the presence of a notary public who will then complete the notary block. You will also need to have two witnesses sign the form.

Part III. General Provisions included in the Directive and Durable Power of Attorney (Continued)

YOU MUST SIGN THIS DOCUMENT IN THE PRESENCE OF TWO WITNESSES.

IN WITNESS WHEREOF, I have executed this document this _____ day of _____(month), _____(year).

_____
Signature

Print Name _____
Address _____

_____

The person who signed this document is of sound mind and voluntarily signed this document in our presence. Each of the undersigned witnesses is at least eighteen years of age.

Signature _____   Signature _____
Print Name_____   Print Name _____
Address _____   Address _____

_____   _____

ONLY REQUIRED FOR PART I — DURABLE POWER OF ATTORNEY

STATE OF MISSOURI   )
) SS
COUNTY OF _____   )

On this _____ day of _____ (month), _____ (year), before me personally appeared _____, to me known to be the person described in and who executed the foregoing instrument and acknowledged that he/she executed the same as his/her free act and deed.

IN WITNESS WHEREOF, I have hereunto set my hand and affixed my official seal in the County of _____, State of Missouri, the day and year first above written.

_____
Notary Public

My Commission Expires:

244

Ordering Information

Additional copies of this form are available at courthouses, libraries, and University of Missouri Extension Centers across Missouri at no charge. The form may be photocopied for use by additional persons. The form may also be ordered directly from The Missouri Bar. Single copies of the form are available from The Missouri Bar at no charge. However, a charge has been placed on multiple copies in order to cover the costs of printing, handling and postage. A check or money order for the correct amount must be sent to The Missouri Bar before multiple copies of the form may be mailed.

To order multiple copies of the form, refer to the pricing chart below.

PRICE CHART

Single copes .... No charge
Additional copies .... 75 center per copy

Please send a written request for the number of copies you desire, along with a check or money order for the correct amount, to:

Health Care Proxy Form
The Missouri Bar
P.O. Box 119
Jefferson City, MO 65102-0119

..... From The Missouri Bar To You

This health care decisions form has been developed as a project of The Missouri Bar, the statewide association for all lawyers. Working for the public good, The Missouri Bar strives to improve the law and the administration of justice.

Revised March, 2005

The following is downloaded from A/PACT:

Aging Parents and Adult Children Together (A/PACT)

ALTERNATIVES TO GUARDIANSHIP

(Sixth in a 10-part series)

Your 82-year-old father is overwhelmed with financial documents and gets confused and frustrated when he sorts through them. He often accidentally overdraws his checking account or forgets to pay bills. His only income is Social Security, so he has to be careful with his money. You're concerned he can't manage his financial affairs any longer. Should you petition for guardianship?

Adult children often are faced with evidence that a parent is no longer keeping up with his or her personal finances or is making financial decisions that are inconsistent with past spending habits. Your immediate reaction should not be to petition a court to appoint a guardian.

A guardian or, in some states, a conservator, is a person appointed by a court to decide financial or personal matters for another person who is unable to manage his or her own affairs. A guardianship, or conservatorship, however, is a severe deprivation of a person's right to make his or her own decisions. It should be considered only after other methods of protecting the person fail.

You can explore various legal options with your parent to help manage their assets. Your parent can choose from several simple legal documents designed to give you or some-

247

one else — an agent — the authority to manage some or all matters, usually financial, on their behalf.

A power of attorney lets your parent appoint a person they trust — an *agent* or *attorney-in-fact* — to help manage their finances. It's fairly simple and inexpensive to create a power of attorney. Urge your parent to talk with a lawyer about the specific responsibilities that can be given to an agent. It may be reassuring for them to know that the agent they select is there to help them carry out their wishes.

A person who signs a power of attorney is called a *principal*. To sign a power of attorney, a person must be mentally competent. That means the principal must understand what he or she is doing and want to delegate certain decision-making responsibilities to someone else. Importantly, the agent can continue handling the principal's finances if the principal becomes incompetent but only if the power of attorney specifically states that the principal wants the document to remain in effect after his or her incapacity. This crucial clause makes the power of attorney *durable*. An ordinary power of attorney becomes useless when the principal becomes mentally incapacitated.

A person also can designate when the durable power of attorney goes into effect. It can start when the document is signed or at some other time, say, when the principal becomes incapacitated. This latter type of power of attorney is called springing, because it springs into effect in the future. With a springing power of attorney, a principal must clearly define how others should determine that the *springing* event has occurred. All powers of attorney end when the principal dies, unless the document specifies an earlier date. The principal also can change or revoke a power of attorney at any time.

A power of attorney can be very specific or very general, depending on the principal's wishes. He or she can authorize just one thing, like selling a car, or include everything that the principal could do him- or herself. Suggest that your parent get legal advice to help understand how to tailor the power of attorney to fit his or her wishes and needs.

There are several other protective tools. A person who receives income from Social Security may ask the Social Security Administration to appoint a *representative payee* to receive the monthly checks and use the money to pay his or her living expenses. The payee must open a separate bank account where the checks will be deposited electronically by Direct Deposit. The representative payee has no authority over any of the recipient's other funds and must report to the Social Security Administration annually, showing how the money was spent to meet the beneficiary's needs.

To have a representative payee appointed, you or your parent must fill out a form stating that your parent cannot manage the Social Security benefits. Include a letter from your parent's doctor as confirmation. The Social Security Administration will accept recommendations concerning who should be appointed the payee, but is not required to follow them.

Your parent can establish a *living trust* — a legal arrangement by which he or she transfers ownership of assets to another person — the *trustee*. The trustee must manage the assets on behalf of the people designated as the trust's *beneficiaries*. The same person can simultaneously serve as the creator of the trust (the *grantor* or *settlor*), the trustee and the beneficiary. However, older people who are not prepared to be the trustee can still be the beneficiary during their lifetime, and direct the trustee to distribute any remaining assets to secondary beneficiaries after their death.

More complex trusts also are available, but usually are not appropriate for people with limited assets. You and your parent should consult with a lawyer to evaluate whether a trust would be suitable and to determine the most appropriate type of trust.

When the alternatives discussed here and in "Daily Money Management Programs" (the seventh column in this series) have been exhausted, or if you know your parent is not capable of putting any plan into effect, you may need to consider a guardianship or conservatorship. Consult with an attorney to determine the appropriate course of action.

For More Information

Social Security: A Guide for Representative Payees, Social Security Pub. No. 05-10076. Call (800) 772-1213 to order.

American Association of Retired Persons
Fulfillment
601 E Street, NW
Washington, DC 20049
www.aarp.org/getans/wills.html
AARP publishes *Tomorrow's Choices*, Stock No. D13479, and *Wills and Living Trusts*, Stock No. D14535.

National Academy of Elder Law Attorneys
1604 North Country Club Road
Tucson, AZ 85716
(520) 881-4005; fax: (520) 325-7925
www.naela.com

Prepared by the American Association of Retired Persons

Eric's Comments

I believe in any "alternative to guardianship" you can figure out, if at all possible. This presentation is meant to be informative and hopefully can help with definitions. If you are going "face to face" in getting a full guardianship, it probably is an emotional "lose, lose" situation. Once you gain guardianship, not only are you in control but you are also mentally, emotionally, and legally liable for the person's well being. This is an awesome responsibility. I recommend Advance Directives so you know the end-of-life wishes of your elderly loved one. I believe in providing all possible help and support. Joint accounts, where you arrange for statements to be sent to you, work well. I believe in having a relationship with the bank so you are notified if there is something out of the ordinary happening in an account. This is also recommended for other types of investment accounts, assets, etc. You can obtain a "springing power of attorney," which allows you to function in the event the elderly can no longer function. The most common are for health care decisions.

Actually, in our family, my folks put everything in trust and my oldest brother was one of the trustees. This allowed him to conduct and attend to their financial matters with them. It is important that we allow the elderly to remain as independent as possible. As they lose their ability to handle things, we should gently help and gain control by compassion, not Courts. The Court is the last resort! You sort of become your parents' Guardian Angel. (We don't ever see Guardian Angels; we just know they're there.) A Care Manager generally can help in these situations when families live out of the elderly's area.

27.
Grieving

I've touched on grieving and multiple end-of-life issues. It is important for us to understand that grieving is an individual emotion. There is no "one size fits all." Grieving is personal, emotional, and maybe not rationale. Grieving can be handled in many different ways and, if they work, all are correct. Grieving is a natural, normal, emotional reaction to loss.

I view life as a journey. We are always moving. We are always in transition, sometimes good, sometimes bad, but always in transition. This transition is not a steady curving line starting from nothing, building, and then ending at nothing. It is a curving line full of wavering peaks and valleys. It does, however, start and end with nothing. My wife believes the journey is eternal within God. The goal is to move the final declining line as far out as possible.

As we journey, there may be greater or lesser distances between the peaks and valleys. We'll have good decades and good years. As we age, distances shrink. We have a good year, good month, good week and, at the end, some good days and moments. Grieving is a part of our journey. One of the physics of our journey is: we can't go back. We can never be younger. We can't bring back a lost loved one. We can't go back, and we can't avoid loss.

I have lived a charmed life. I've had all sorts of problems; relationship, health, financial, etc. However, I didn't experience a death of a close relative until I was in my fifties. I lost a good friend just out of high school, but it was different. I can still remember his name and how senseless his death was, but it was still different.

In my fifties, I lost my wife of 34 years and both my Mom and Dad within a few years. I've been told that losing a life partner is the worst loss you can experience. I think perhaps losing a child or grandchild could be even worse. The experts seem to think that your life partner would help you through the grief of losing close relatives, yet many couples who have faced the death of a child eventually divorce. For those of you reading this who have lost children, I pray for you. I can't begin to imagine your loss. The only help I can offer is that life is a journey and somehow you have to take the next steps.

I've been noted for being a "hit 'em head-on" type of guy. I'm going to offer you my grieving techniques for you to consider. Remember, I'm sharing what worked for me. Take what you like from this and leave the rest.

The physics of grieving is; until you pass through it, you are still in it! This is a journey, and I recommend you keep moving. I think that one of the most important tools is to recognize you are hurt. Admit you are sad. You can't avoid the pain. You can stall the pain. You can put it off but you can't avoid it. I encourage you to feel it. Feel every bit of the terrible loss. Don't shy away from it. In business, I'm a "worst first" person. Get the most terrible or worst tasks out of the way first. Do the thing that you dread the most,and then you don't have to dread it anymore.

My wife died one week before Christmas. She died on our daughter's birthday. My wife's favorite holiday was Christmas. Our house was decorated with her favorite ornaments and decorations. Presents were under the tree. It was going to be a perfect holiday. One problem; she died. My children are grown and no longer lived at home, so there I was, stockings hung by the chimney with care. You talk about sad.

We made the arrangements and had the funeral.

While you are in this mode, there are activities to keep you busy. You're still doing things for the departed. They still need you. It hasn't sunk in yet! Then it was three days until Christmas. What would we do, how would we handle it? My kids with their spouses, my grandson, and I had a meeting. This was a terrible event for us all. We asked the question, "What do we do?" Our answer was to not avoid the pain. We decided to carry out all of the original plans, including the dinner we had planned, and open all of the gifts; even the ones from Mom. This part still pains me when I think about it. We knew it would be hard but we thought it would be easier to feel the terrible Christmas hurt then to put it off till next year. It was terrible. It was sad. We cried. We grieved our Christmas loss. I'm not sure I can paint the right picture for this sadness.

The day after Christmas, we took down my wife's decorations. The kids took the items that meant the most to them while their memories were still fresh. Now as I look back, five years later, I know we did the right thing. Each Christmas gets better because we let it all out during the first one. We didn't avoid the pain, we didn't try to keep a stiff upper lip; we cried! We took an important first step in our journey of grieving. We recognized our loss and allowed ourselves to feel our loss. We didn't run. We didn't hide. We didn't deny. We didn't stop living. We cried!

Loss is part of the life cycle. In a way, the deeper the love, the greater the pain. To protect yourself from loss, you would have to avoid love and bonding to others. When you feel the deep pains of grief, be reminded of how fortunate you were to have had someone for whom you deeply cared. When I met Ann, I was still acutely aware of the sense of loss of a loved one. One of my considerations was whether or not to get involved again. Would I protect myself from the possible pain of loss? If I had done this, I would have missed out on a wonderful woman who creates a wonderful life for us today. You can't have happiness without the risk of sadness.

I believe you are going to shed an appropriate number of tears as you grieve a loss. I don't think you can avoid shedding these tears. I personally believe that many people can decide when they are going to shed them. The longer you wait and the more you keep these feelings bottled up, the worse it will be.

Think of this analogy. You have a tire on your car that is losing air. It is a slow leak although you know it needs to be repaired. It's nearly flat when you first become aware of the true extent of the problem, so you have it aired up. It lasts for a while, but you have to put more air in it. You have a lot of stuff to do. So much stuff that you don't think you have time to have it repaired. On the other hand, you have so much stuff to do that you sure can't have it go all the way flat. You'll then have bigger problems. You know how much trouble a flat will cause you, so you start to worry about the tire going flat. You keep checking it, adding air to it, and trying make it last. After all, you have too much stuff to do to get it fixed. Then you have a little time for yourself and decide to take a drive. You're relaxed, driving, and suddenly you remember that you haven't checked the tire. Now you are really concerned. You agonize, you worry, you're fearful, yet you drive on. After all you've been through, you deserve this break.

Through your entire drive or vacation, your well-deserved down time, you've been consumed by your fears, worries, anxieties, pent-up emotions, and the rest of the issues you've put on hold. No matter where you go and no matter what you do, your leaking tire is on your mind. By now, most of you have probably determined that, if this were your tire, you would have fixed it at the first sign of trouble. You would know that, in the long run, it would save you time, trouble, and grief to deal with the issue up front. I'm not trying to compare the loss of a loved one to blowing out your left front radial tire although I am trying to get you to think about how we approach loss. Nobody can tell you how it makes you feel. Nobody can tell you how long it will take to get it into livable, manageable proportions. I can tell you it is a journey and it is important to keep moving. If you stop moving, you are stuck at the point in your journey where you stopped.

Another small analogy: Twenty-five years ago I had a major aorta femoral by-pass operation. It was my first surgery of any kind and, leading up to it, I was terrified. I couldn't imagine the pain I was going to endure. I remember telling the doctor to give me enough pain medicine to allow me to sleep through the pain until I went home. When I awoke in the recovery room, I was obviously in a great deal of pain. This is the pain I had dreaded. The doctor did as I requested and kept me heavily medicated. I remember trying my best to avoid moving. I complained and was very difficult when the nurses tried to get me to move or walk. I took the dope and hoped this would all pass.

During the first couple of days, I developed a respiratory infection because I wouldn't cough up the matter in my lungs. It hurt and I was afraid of the pain that coughing would cause. After about a week, they started taking me off the pain medication. When I tried to move, I was weak, sore, and every part of my body hurt. You can't lay motionless on dope for a week without causing some problems. I was 39 years old, yet I had become feeble. I entered the hospital strong and was going to leave weak. When I got home, it took me quite awhile to get my strength back. My recovery took longer than I thought it would. Wow, this was absolutely as bad as I had feared.

In the past couple of years, I have had multiple surgeries on my legs. One surgery consisted of removing a vein from my right leg and placing it in my left leg. The incisions ran from my groin to mid calf on each leg. I told my wife that I was in a quandary. I didn't know which leg to limp on. Remember, I'm the guy who is afraid of the pain

257

and who would do anything to avoid it. Guess what? I got it figured out. They'd tried to tell me in the first surgery, but I wouldn't listen. As soon as the nursing staff will let you get up and walk, do it! Sure it hurts, but you still have your natural body strength. You haven't become weak from inactivity. The quicker you get your range of motion back, the less pain you feel. You work out the kinks and recover much quicker. It isn't that it doesn't hurt; it just doesn't hurt as long. You get it behind you. Face it, do it, and move on. Take my word for it, it is a lot less painful in the long run. The quicker I try to return to a normal schedule, the quicker I recover. I don't skip any steps. I keep on moving. My advice is to figure out where you want to be when you get to the other side; then figure out how you are going to get there. I don't mean you'll know the nuts and bolts of where you want to be, but you may have an idea of where you want to be emotionally.

I recognize that each situation is different and this may not work for everyone. It is an option to consider. We all have our own individual timelines based on our particular loss and situation. I once heard denial defined as, "a subconscious defense mechanism we use to protect ourselves from losses too deep to currently bear." According to my wife, my approach is that of a pretty tough, strong, assertive guy. She believes I am emotionally strong and points out that I had physically cared for my wife and parents years before their passing. Also, I had my opportunities to say, "I love you" and complete unfinished emotional business with my parents. Even though Judy was ill for a few years, she died unexpectedly. The only way to keep from having unfinished business is to keep your emotional business caught up each day. Treat each day as though it is your last. I knew that I had given them my best. This points out the importance of saying and hearing all that you and they need to hear and say.

Whatever your situation, the only way around it is through it. Faith is certainly the most important help you can have. I wish you well on your journey.

28.
Does Society Really Care About Our Elders?

There are other cultures that do a better job of keeping home and caring for elders than we do. We had a meeting not too long ago for people dealing with aging parents. At the same time, there was a community meeting concerning gang activity and violence in our area. The leading television station sponsored the gang violence meeting. They did in-depth reports on local gang activity and went all out to raise public awareness about area gangs and their activities. They promoted it for two weeks and reported numerous stories of graffiti to prove the existence of greater gang presence in our area than what was thought. They partnered with the Community Foundation which had some funding to deal with this problem. It was an area-wide blitz and probably accurate and worthwhile.

I'm a "senior advocate" and don't believe senior issues get the attention they deserve. Our meeting was held to discuss in-home senior safety issues and was targeted toward adult children as well as seniors. I've written two booklets, "How Safe is Your Senior's Home?" and "Eleven Signs Your Aging Parents Need Help," which I gave away to attendees. We wrote, e-mailed, and faxed all radio, TV stations, and print media in our area. I spoke with a local newspaper reporter to try to get some attention in the paper. The reporter was dealing with an aging parent and seemed personally very interested. We spoke for over thirty minutes and I felt good about the possibility of coverage. I did two live radio shows and was interviewed by two other radio stations the day before the event. I also mailed invitations to over 150 local churches. I cited statistics stating that the leading cause of accidental deaths in people seventy-four and older was from falls. Also, Emergency Room visits and nursing home admissions for falls are numerous. I even thought up this slogan for older moms or grandmothers using a step stool; "stairway to heaven." Throw rugs could be a "fast track to the nursing home; just slide on in." My wife was less than enthusiastic toward my creative attempts. It's no laughing matter when it applies to you or your fragile elderly mother. Watching someone lie in a nursing home as a result of an injury that could have been prevented is also no laughing matter.

The gang violence meeting drew over four-hundred people; my meeting drew five. The gang violence TV promos showed two incidents involving elderly women that occurred during the past year; nothing fatal or causing any physical harm, just frightening incidents and property loss. It made good promotional material. One of the five people at my meeting discussed an issue she had with her mother. I mentioned the need to have good lighting at night when the elderly move about so they won't trip and fall. She told us that her mother was so afraid that someone would know she was home alone and vulnerable that she refused to turn on any lights after dark. The daughter was concerned about her mother's safety. We talked of different forms of illuminations such as light strips, glowing switch pads, etc., to improve her mother's safety.

The thought occurred to me that this was a good example of unintended consequences. The mother's family lived next door in a well lit, safe neighborhood that probably never reported an incident of violence, let alone gang activity. The mother was far more at risk from a fall than a gang attack. She was frightened, which caused a very unsafe reaction. We need to be sure that we understand how the elderly process information they receive. It is entirely possible that an unfounded fear will lead to an unsafe reaction. I continue to try to raise the level of awareness about aging issues and elder safety. We need to ensure a safe living arrangement for our elderly loved ones wherever they reside.

I predict that due to the aging of the huge Baby Boomer population there will be a lot more interest in senior issues and a lot more services to help us age as we would like.

29.

Conclusion

A Simple Plan

Over the next twenty years the pressure will increase dramatically on health care delivery in the United States. The Baby Boomer generation accounts for approximately twenty-eight percent of the population. In twenty years the boomers age will be from sixty-four to eight-two years old. Life expectancies are increasing. The current aging population already has a desire to "age in place." People want to remain active and independent for as long as possible. The Hospice Model also verifies an individual's desire to die in their own bed.

Health Care providers, Insurance Companies, and progressive companies have been putting wellness programs in place as incentives for a healthier population. Society is attacking unhealthy practices and lifestyles Through mass media campaigns. There are groups formed to combat hunger, obesity, liquor, smoking, fat, caffeine, reckless driving, cell phone use while driving, fires, thefts, aggressive behavior, and many other detrimental activities. There are laws and regulations for drugs, alcohol, tobacco, seat belt use, helmet use on motorcycles, as well as countless other safety measures. We have services for suicide prevention, family violence, battered women shelters, rape crisis centers, nursery crisis centers, substance abuse centers, counseling centers, children's services, and many other help services. We have created countless "not for profit" organizations to help the homeless, the poor, the downtrodden. *Who's looking out for our seniors?*

According to the 2005 Missouri Senior Report only 7.5% of Greene County's senior population was living in poverty. This report lists the 2005 population estimate at 34,759 individuals 65+ years of age. In 2000 the average household income listed was $39,821 and 78.5% of this population was living in owner-occupied housing with a median value of $88,200. The Department of Health and Senior Services lists 2,240 licensed beds at Skilled Nursing Facilities in Greene County. While the seniors think of these places as the "nursing home," they actually provide long-term care for individuals of any age. The majority will be issues of aging but not all. There are a total of 548 beds in RCF One and Two facilities and 281 licensed assisted living beds. U.S. census projections for Missouri for 2025 indicate a population increase in those 65+ years old of 62.5%. If you use that as a factor for Greene County, the projected 65+ population for the year 2025 would be 77,333 people. The current population break down is 51% are 65-74; 35% are 74-85; and 14% are 85+. Using this distribution for the year 2025, our population over eight-five will be 10,826 individuals. *How are we going to care for them?*

Currently our aging population is served predominately by the Southwest Missouri Office on Aging. The Community Partnership of the Ozarks sponsors Senior Link which serves mostly as a networking opportunity. The Department of Health and Senior Services maintains an Elder Abuse hotline and provides area employees to work with reported problems. The State offers help to low income seniors through Medicaid programs.

The fact is that the population is aging! Today's model for services is "reactive." We generally treat the results of accidents, malnutrition and diminished capacities by institutionalization. In the future, there simply will not be enough beds or services using the current model. We need to become "proactive" toward the aging of our population.

Senior safety is of the utmost importance in this change. Addressing senior nourishment, medications, transportation, living arrangements, social networking, and assistance with daily living activities can help seniors maintain their independence longer. We also must develop better, more economical methods to deliver care in the senior's home.

Goal:

To keep our elder population out of the emergency room, hospital, skilled nursing facility, or nursing home for as long as possible!

Plan:

Create a physician group that specializes in keeping individuals in their own homes. This group should encourage the use of either Physician Assistants or Nurse Practitioners to make affordable "house calls." We should put pressure where needed to get the necessary reimbursements from Medicare, Medicaid, or private insurance to cover these costs. This group's facility should also be easy for the elderly to access and negotiate. Based on population demographics, the bulk of patients will be Medicare, Private Insurance, or Private Pay. This specialized group must offer acceptable, accessible, affordable services.

Medically necessary services that are customarily reimbursed by others should be delivered by the appropriate health care providers. These services should be more closely monitored by the Physician Group than the current model provides. Non-medical in-home services should be provided by approved, qualified suppliers that do not provide medical care. This will allow for the delivery of in-home custodial care at more reasonable costs.

This program should be marketed by insurance carriers as a senior wellness program. There should be incentives developed for patients who will participate in this program as well as the assurance that the providers are determined to do what it takes to "keep them home."

Incentives for:
- In-home safety inspections and, if reported, defects are corrected
- Driver re-training for older drivers
- Fall prevention techniques
- Medication reviews
- Utilization of in-home assistance
- Utilization of transportation assistance
- Diet and nutritional review and recommendations
- Regular medical check-ups

Somehow we need to reward the individual for compliance; either by reduced costs, special recognitions, a promotional reward, or some other new idea.

The Last Lap
As I view the aging process, it is important for me to reinforce the fact that I am a student of "life" and my classroom has been my life to date. I observe people living and feeling life. We all have our methods of "knowing" we are still alive. We have measures of what is an acceptable quality of life.

Our acceptance levels change as we age. When we are young, we learn, and mature by testing and ever increasing our boundaries. As we age, we continually attempt to, at least, not lose any of our capabilities we've worked so hard to obtain. In our elder years, we must learn to accept our diminishing abilities. We decline at various ages, often because of new health challenges.

I believe we engage in certain activities to "feel" we are alive. For example: An older person may go to a local mall and walk for an hour every day. Granted, it is excellent exercise, but we continue to walk for the feeling of being alive that day. We know we are alive and still maintaining an acceptable level of activity.

I had a relative who played golf. He had very poor circulation which kept him from doing the activity he loved. He was in his eighties and agreed to undergo risky surgery to repair his circulation. When asked about the risk of death, his response was, "I'm willing to risk death to be able to enjoy what life I have left." He had established a quality-of-life standard that allowed him to feel alive. He died from complications from the surgery. The people who survived him realized it was his choice to make.

To me, he set his standard too high. He had family who loved and enjoyed him. He was able to travel, read, watch TV, surf the net, and socialize with his family. Acceptance of our actual abilities is always hard.

We need to make friends with our aging process. We need to be as active and healthy as we can, but we should not place artificial benchmarks for ourselves. Sometimes the risks we face to prove we still can perform a certain function are far greater than the reward for the performance. If I used to be able to climb a mountain, that's great. If I try to climb the same mountain after I have lost physical ability just to prove "I still can do it," I can achieve disastrous results. I could have a stroke, heart attack, fall and break something, or, at best, be full of aches and pains. If I overdo, I may have to skip walking anywhere for awhile. What did I prove? Who cares besides me? I'm not saying don't do it if you still can do it without complications. I am saying, "Don't do it just to prove you can do it." What do you prove if you can't? Plus, what have you put at risk?

I like to eat at buffets. I may have already mentioned my end-of-life philosophy? I also believe, "'Don't let the skinny people plan the picnic." However, this is my book and I'm getting older just writing it, so bear with me on the redundancy. I like to play golf, but now I can't. I enjoy watching others play. I like to water-ski, but now I can't. I enjoy watching others ski. I like playing football and baseball, but now I can't. I enjoy watching others play. I like making love, but now I can't. I enjoy...wait a minute, I can still do that. I'm not dead yet. I can still go on vacation with my wife, who loves me, and watch sunsets. I can watch my grandchildren play. I can feel moved at church and help someone else. We should accept our new lives and enjoy as much as we can. I told my family that one of my favorite things to do is eat the food buffet on a cruise ship. I've set my benchmark at an appropriate level. Make friends with your new future. Don't give up or quit trying, just use some common sense. After all, there's nothing like an old fool. As long as someone can get me to the buffet line on the cruise ship, I'll continue on!

One lap of my life I hope to avoid is the nursing home lap. I don't see any buffets or beaches at the nursing homes I could afford. I believe that in many cases it is an artificial extension of life. Granted, come hell or high water, some of us are going to end up in the "home." Many of us aren't going to like it when we get there.

Remember Skippy, the friendly dog who got sent away? As I wrote his story, I tried to indicate that his master had the good sense, commitment, and resources to take Skippy home. But what if he didn't? What would have happened to Skippy? At home, Skippy had a very relaxed routine. After he went out for his morning stroll, he napped for a while. His owner put food in his dish so Skippy could eat at his leisure. No problems, no worries. Skippy could patrol the house through the day. He could bark at the mailman. He could move to various windows to lie in the sun. His water dish was always tended since he was the only dog in the house. No problems, no worries. Sometimes people rang the door bell, so Skippy barked to alert them that he was there to protect his master's property. He had a purpose; he enjoyed his life. No problems, no worries.

Let's look in on him at the doggy nursing home. The vast majority of dogs don't want to be here. Unless they have quite a bit of money, they are placed, two each, in small rooms. They must share their potty tree and TV. The place is pretty clean and very bright. There are a lot more dogs than there are people to care for them.

Early each morning they must get up, even if they have little to do the rest of the day. They must "do their business" and then head for breakfast. They are led into a room to be fed. Some dogs can no longer feed themselves, so Skippy watches as someone helps them. Watching them drool and slobber doesn't help Skippy's appetite. The food is okay, but since some dogs have different digestive problems, most of the food is unseasoned and bland. It sure isn't as good as at home. Skippy misses the special treats he got at home.

Well, we're through with breakfast; now, what do we do? Many of us don't want to be here anyway. Some of the older mutts amuse each other but, for the most part, we all sit at the door waiting to get out or for someone to come visit us. We spend our time hanging around waiting. I'm not sure what we're waiting for? Occasionally we will have a visitor. Maybe just before Christmas some puppies will come by and howl for us.

Most of us are unhappy here even though the staff tells everybody how happy we are. In order to keep us from being so miserable they give us psychotropic medication to help us be calm and less depressed. Oh, for those good old hippy days! It is a lot different now. We take our medicine, eat, and we wait. What are we waiting for? We get more frail, our coat grays, we become more feeble. If we get sick they give us medicines and feed us through I.V.'s or tubes. Sometimes we may even be taken to a hospital so we can get better and come back. Maybe this isn't even what we want? Perhaps we are tired and want to go to our Heavenly Father's home where we will no longer feel pain and will be reunited with loved ones who have gone before us. We wait. What are we waiting for? We look around our room; no bones, no family, only the old dog beside us. He sees the same things we see.

Our possessions are the two collars we brought, our doggy tooth brush, and our little doggy slippers.

If we are lucky, our owner visits once in a while. Our puppies are grown and have lives of their own. We wouldn't want to be a burden.

Our roommate was once proud as well. He reacted with anger when they took away his bone. He too was declared vicious. He too gets medication to control his rage, his fear, his disappointment. He too would like to be home with a bone, his family, his possessions and his fondest memories.

Going home is the only hope we cling to. We take the medicine. We wait to go home. Maybe today! Only this time, home will be our Heavenly home. This is not the life we were seeking.

How have we as a society become so callous, egotistical, and self-righteous to believe we should control when, where, and how Skippy dies? How have we gotten so far away from a natural, dignified end-of-life? Why do we all put so much importance on quantity of life over quality of life? How many people have you heard say, "By God, I want to live and draw every breath I can, no matter how miserable it makes me. I want to be kept alive with tubes, pumps, valves, sprockets, gears and anything available, even if I have no idea who or where I am. Be sure I end up somewhere far from my belongings. Make life as difficult as possible for my loved ones. Life is precious even if I have no knowledge of it."

I've yet to meet anyone with these desires. I come under constant criticism. People tell me the old folks are safer and better off in the nursing home. Well, Skippy and I aren't buying it! Granted, some people have no choice. It may be the best solution for some. Each situation is different. Some families have no resources. Some don't want to be bothered. They've bought the story, "The old folks are better off." In my opinion, some buy it because there is less personal responsibility involved. We can clean our hands of responsibility. After all, who wants to be responsible for their Mom or Dad's death? I did and I'm glad. Left to the current model, they would have died a death that was the most terrifying to them. I have peace of mind knowing that they died the way they wanted to die; with dignity. One final time, this is not for everyone.

There are many "volunteer family" caregivers who are wonderful individuals and I applaud you. You are very loving, caring people who are giving up your lives for someone else. You are truly unique.

I view the current elder care model as "reactive" and feel it should become "proactive, preventive." In this writing, I may appear to be critical of health care and I don't mean to be. My son is an RN and Nurse Manager. His wife is a EEG Registered Tech. Both work for a local hospital. I sincerely feel that the vast majority of people working in the delivery of health services care not only for the elderly but for all of us, and are very good at what they do. The same is true for the people involved in nursing facilities. My complaint is with the structure and bureaucracy, not with the people involved.

There are families that do not have sufficient resources to care for their elderly. Some elderly are better served in the social setting of a nursing home. There are some family relationships so damaged that compassionate care is virtually impossible to expect. We reap what we sow.

This book is written for those families that have enough resources available to provide paid caregivers. By using outside help, you are able to maintain a better relationship with your elders. You both have your own lives to live. The company I founded is designed to give people their lives back. Our employees are truly doing "God's" work. They are caring, nurturing, loving individuals needing to work yet aren't in it for the money alone. It is a way for a senior worker to give back and have meaningful work at the end of his or her career.

As my wife Ann worked on editing and "smoothing" this book, I observed some unexpected feelings. She explained that she did not have the same nurturing relationship with her mother that I had with my parents. My relationship with my parents was not warm and fuzzy either, until they declined and needed help. The only way I could get along peacefully with my Dad through the years was to stay away from him. I continually had to protect myself emotionally from him. It was a struggle but, in the end, I had some very good years with Mom and Dad in spite of our disagreements.

There is one major difference between the end of Ann's mother's life and my folks'. The company I've since founded did not exist. I did not change Depends, bathe my parents, clean their ears, cut their toenails, or provide any personal grooming. I cooked because I love to cook and eat. I didn't provide care; I oversaw the delivery of care. I ensured the quality and the availability of care. I did not deliver it. Ann did exactly the same, she just had fewer options available.

I predict there will be many non-medical companies created to deliver in-home care to the elderly in the future. Boomers will expect and demand these services. The purpose of my writing this book is to share my experiences as well as get you to seek options for care. It is imperative that we create better end-of-life circumstances for our elderly. I have heard aging compared to a bottle of fine wine: "It gets better with age." The question is, "How long does it last after the cork has popped?"

As you begin your journey, either with an elderly loved one or yourself, I encourage you to take my father's advice and "Think Ahead of Disaster."